A BOOK OF TROUT FLIES

A BOOK of TROUT FLIES

Containing A List of the Most Important American Stream Insects & Their Imitations

BY PRESTON J. JENNINGS

ILLUSTRATED BY ALMA W. FRODERSTROM

With a New Introduction by ERNEST SCHWIEBERT, a Foreword by HERMAN T. SPIETH, PH.D., and an Afterword by EUGENE V. CONNETT, 3RD ~ ~

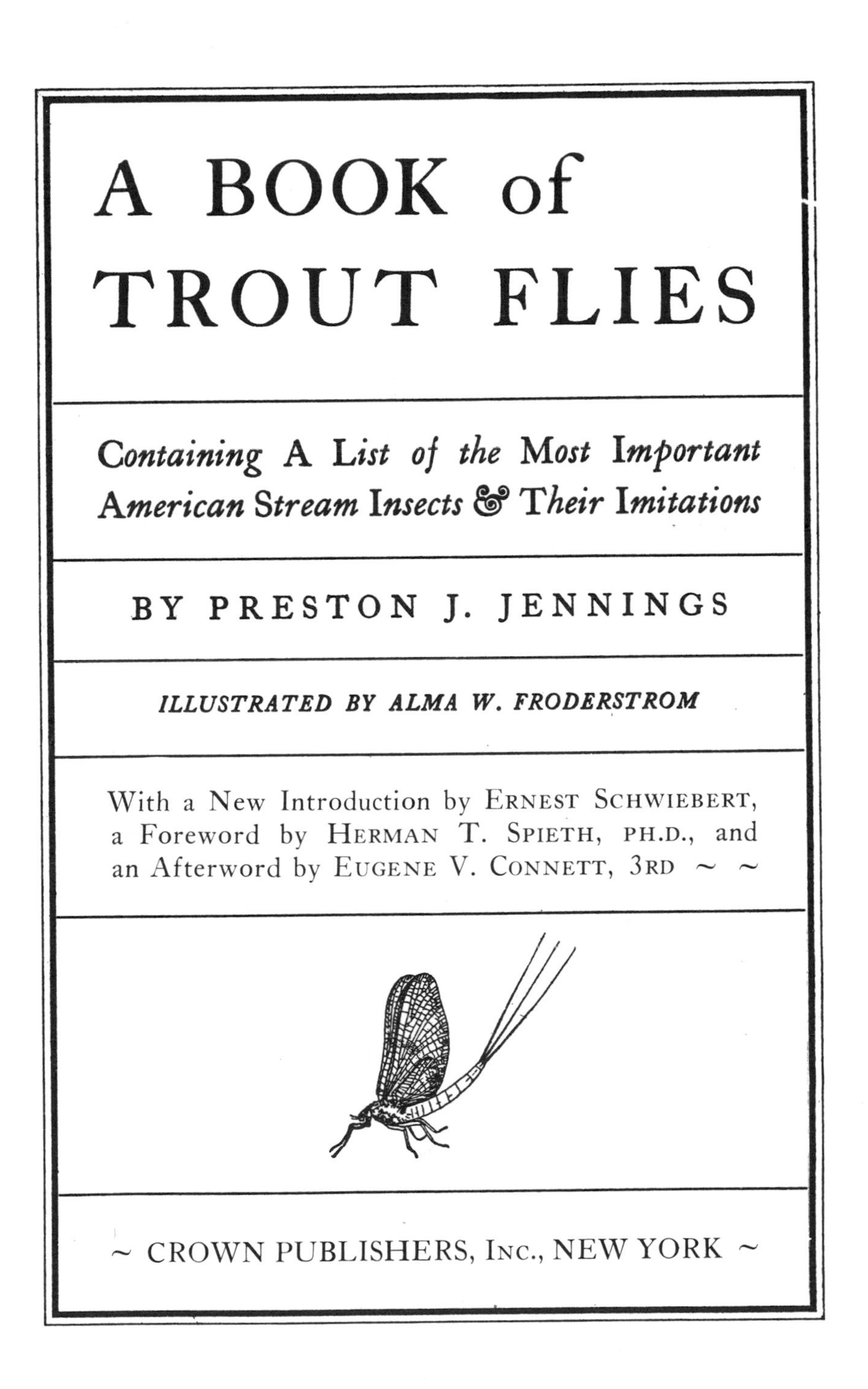

~ CROWN PUBLISHERS, INC., NEW YORK ~

DEDICATION

THIS BOOK IS DEDICATED TO MY WIFE

ADELE MARIE LOUISE

WHO SITS COMPLACENTLY ON THE BANK

WITH HER KNITTING

AND LETS ME ATTEND TO THE FISHING

MAY TIME BE AS GENEROUS WITH HER

AS SHE HAS BEEN KIND AND

CONSIDERATE OF ME

LIBRARY OF CONGRESS CATALOG CARD NUMBER: 70–127495

Printed in the United States of America

Published simultaneously in Canada by General Publishing Company Limited

Second Printing, February, 1971

INTRODUCTION *to the 1970 Edition*

ALMOST a half century has passed since the British angler John Waller Hills observed, in his vintage *A History of Fly Fishing for Trout,* that angling has evolved through cycles of innovation and classicism. His argument has survived the perspective of centuries.

Running parallel to this evolution is a contrapuntal theme of concern with fly-fishing entomology. Its focus is the intricate relationship between stream insects and fly-dressing and the cyclical feeding rhythms of the trout. Entomology and imitation of the primary hatches are centuries-old tools of angling, with origins as ancient as the rivers of third-century Macedonia.

The writings of Dame Juliana Berners emerged six centuries ago in the cloisters of Sopwell nunnery, and her *Treatyse of Fysshynge wyth an Angle* included twelve fly patterns that were an effort at matching the hatch. Her classic dozen appeared again in the books of Leonard Mascall and Gervase Markham until Walton was published in 1653.

Charles Cotton was the innovator who followed with his remarkable "Being Instructions How to Angle for Trout and Grayling in a Clear Stream," which appeared in the edition of *The Compleat Angler* published in 1676. There was so much original material, including considerable emphasis on fly imitations, that Cotton is widely hailed as the father of fly-fishing. Chetham and Saunders and Brookes built their careers on Cotton, and their work is the accumulated wisdom of the seventeenth century.

Charles Bowlker emerged about a half century later, building, like Walton before him, on the work of many earlier angling writers and adding his own genius for fly-making and knowledge of hatches and tactics. His classic *The Art of Angling* appeared in 1747, and easily dominated its field for a century; even Hills confessed in his *History of Fly Fishing* that his fishing began with streamside exposure to Bowlker.

Scotcher followed with his *Flyfisher's Legacy* at the turn of the century, which introduced the disciplined study of stream insects and the first color plates of natural flies. Carroll covered the hatches of the Scottish lowlands in his *Angler's Vade-Mecum,* published in Edinburgh eighteen years later, and Bainbridge appeared at about the same time with his *Fly-Fisher's Guide.* Although these books are milestones, their plates are crudely drawn and the colors are of little practical value.

The vacuum was filled in 1836, with the disciplined scientific identification and accurate color plates that became available to anglers when Alfred Ronalds completed his *Fly-Fisher's Entomology,* the first classic work on trout-stream insects. Ronalds is the full flowering of fly-fishing development since its genesis in Aelian, the logical result of more than two thousand years of sport. There have been more than a dozen editions, although it catalogs only the hatches of Staffordshire and Derbyshire; and its thoroughness became the yardstick for all subsequent work on fly hatches.

That example was equaled in the nineteenth-century chalkstream studies made by Frederic M. Halford on the rivers of Hampshire. Halford codified the sum of fly-fishing knowledge before his time into a rational philosophy, and with the help of brilliant fishermen like Hall and Marryat, his work identified the principal hatches of southern England; books like *Floating Flies and How to Dress Them* and *Dry-Fly Entomology* are classics of angling literature.

Halford has been followed by stream entomologists like Moseley, whose *Dry-Fly Fisherman's Entomology* appeared in 1920, several years after Halford's death. Moseley continued his work with exhaustive studies of British caddis hatches, and the Halford tradition is still alive today. Subsequent books on the fly hatches of Britain have been compiled by writers like Theakston and West and Walker, and the compendium of stream insects thus far is perhaps the *Angler's Entomology,* published by J. R. Harris in recent years, with excellent color photographs of hatches collected and recorded at streamside.

The example of these British writers migrated to America in the years after Halford, and first emerged again in the work of Louis Rhead. His book *American Trout Stream Insects* was printed in 1920, and attempted to catalog the hatches of Catskill rivers, although there was no effort to identify the species with the technical precision of his British counterparts.

The first American work on fly hatches that included modern fly-dressings as well as accurate identification of the insects was the first edition of *A Book of Trout Flies,* completed in 1935 by Preston J. Jennings. Like the appearance of Ronalds in 1836, the work of Jennings a century later set the standard of excellence that has measured all subsequent American work on fly-fishing entomology.

Since its initial Derrydale edition first appeared, covering principal hatches from the Raritan and the Brodheads to the Catskills and their sister rivers farther north, there have been other books on American hatches. Knowledgeable fly-fishermen are familiar with Charles Wetzel and his *Practical Fly-Fishing,* Art Flick and his classic little *Streamside Guide,* and my own *Matching the Hatch,* which appeared in 1955. Each of these later books had its principal inspiration in the work of Jennings, and the exquisite watercolors and drawings in *A Book of Trout Flies* set the standard for illustrations of fly hatches in this country.

The stream studies that resulted in the *Streamside Guide* had both the book and Jennings himself—who often fished with Flick in the golden years of the Schoharie and its Westkill Tavern—as their wellspring and example. My own preoccupation with fly-fishing entomology can be traced to the master fly-dresser, William Blades, who suggested that American hatches were still a relatively untapped lode of material. "I'm too old already," Blades said, "but you have a lot of years left to study our trout-stream insects."

His advice was the genesis of my work, but it was largely forgotten until a friend of the family showed me his exquisite copy of Jennings in the Derrydale edition. Its rich plates were the catalyst that resulted in years of pleasant work astream and the catalog of information that later formed my work.

The advice of Blades and the example of Jennings are still alive today, since our catalog of American fly hatches is far from complete. There is considerable work left, particularly in the rivers of the western states, but *A Book of Trout Flies* was the genesis of serious American fly-fishing entomology. Copies of both the Derrydale and original Crown editions have become treasured volumes in fly-fishing libraries on both sides of the Atlantic—and knowledgeable anglers everywhere will welcome this fresh opportunity to own an American classic.

ERNEST SCHWIEBERT

Princeton, New Jersey
April, 1970

PREFACE

THE material from which this book has been composed was collected by the writer from various sources, for his own information and use, so it is with a feeling of great diffidence that it is released for publication.

The writer is not what might be called "an authority" on the subject of entomology or the study of insects; neither is he what might be called "an expert" fly-fisher. As the entomologists with whom he has come in contact know nothing of fly-fishing, however, and as the average angler fishing our streams knows little or nothing of Entomology, it is to be hoped that the remarks about the artificial flies will be of interest to the entomologist and that the fly-fisher will find something of benefit to his sport in the remarks about the natural flies.

Anglers, and especially writers on the subject of angling, owe a debt of gratitude to all angling writers who have preceded them, for much that we know, or think we know, is the result of actual "trial and error" experiments which have been carried on by those who have gone before.

The author wishes to acknowledge this debt to all writers who have contributed to the sport, and who have influenced him in his own experience.

The author wishes to acknowledge the kindly interest and help of Dr. Herman T. Spieth of the College of the

City of New York and for his work in identifying the natural flies known as the *Ephemeridae* or Mayflies, which constitute the major portion of the flies selected for copying or imitating, and for having read and edited the manuscript of this book from the point of view of the Biologist. He also wishes to thank Dr. J. G. Needham, Dr. Cornelius Betten, Dr. C. H. Curran and Dr. William S. Creighton for their work in identifying the remaining specimens of natural flies shown in the following pages.

Specimens of natural flies and minnows were contributed by the following and are hereby acknowledged with thanks: Willis K. Stauffer, Marjorie Stauffer, Roy Steenrod, Raymond Caunitz, William Henninger, Byron Blanchard, Arthur Flick, Eugene V. Connett, 3rd, and Francis W. Rawle.

Although the third name in the scientific designation of the natural flies mentioned in this book should be in roman rather than italic characters, the author felt that many of his readers would find it less confusing if the entire name were in italics.

PRESTON J. JENNINGS

87 Columbia Heights,
Brooklyn, New York.
July 20, 1935.

CONTENTS

ILLUSTRATIONS

FOREWORD

BRAVE is the man who tries to correlate two highly diverse fields of knowledge, and fortunate, indeed, are we when such a difficult task is well done. Much has been written by scientists and others about trout, their habits, and their food. Likewise, a great deal of attention has been spent on the art of constructing artificial flies devised to capture trout. In a vague way, the fact has been accepted that there is some relationship between a specific kind of insect and the structure of a given artificial fly. Mr. Jennings is the first American writer, however, to make a thorough, systematic effort to correlate the artificial flies with the particular natural flies that inhabit the American streams. Any study of this sort demands a great amount of labor and the accumulation of a mass of data.

To the biologist, it is of interest that trout are able to distinguish between various species of insects even though the insects may be superficially similar. Further, it is a well established fact that the particular species of insects with which Mr. Jennings has dealt are restricted to North America. In the instance of the Mayflies, the species noted in the book are restricted to eastern North America. Closely allied species may exist in England and Europe, but never the identical species.

It follows from this that the American fly-fisher must pattern his flies after the various species that are to be found in the region in which he intends to fish.

In reality, Mr. Jennings' book needs no introduction, for it can well speak for itself. Although it is designed primarily for the fly-fisher, the biologists will also welcome it as a happy addition to the sum total of what is known as knowledge.

HERMAN T. SPIETH

Biological Laboratories
Cold Spring Harbor, Long Island
August 3, 1935

A BOOK OF TROUT FLIES

PART I

DRY-FLIES

1. Iron Blue Dun

2. Dark Quill Gordon

3. Quill Gordon

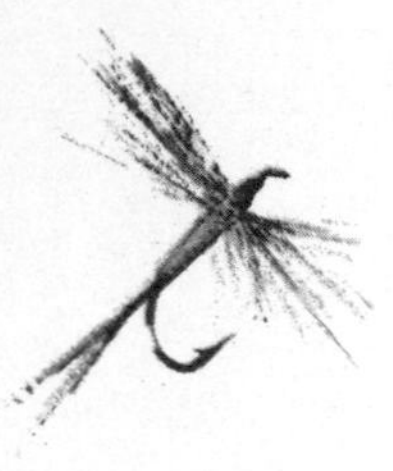

4. Hendrickson

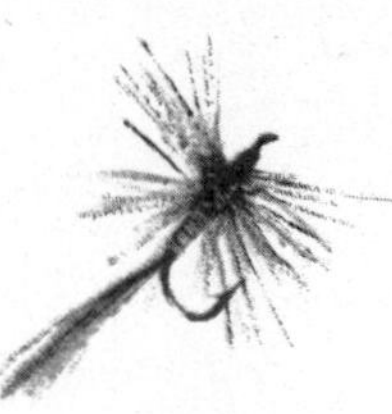

5. Red Quill

6. American March Brown

7. Grey Fox

8. Light Cahill

9. Brown Bi-visible

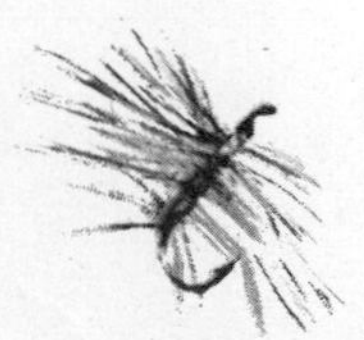

10. Dark Blue Sedge

11. Badger Hackle

12. Little Marryat

CHAPTER I

Naturals

Reduced to fundamentals, fly-fishing is the art of catching fish by means of an artificial fly which suggests to the fish some form of insect life upon which it is accustomed to feed.

The earliest records of fly-fishing, or fishing with a fly, take into consideration the fact that the fish inhabiting a certain river in Macedonia were accustomed to feed on a natural fly known as the "Hippouros," and the first artificial fly of which there is a record was designed to represent this natural fly.

Leonard West, the author of The Trout Fly, suggests that trout flies fall into one of two categories, namely, Attractors or Deceivers. The Attractors are those flies which are frankly lures and are not made with the intention of being copies of any natural insect. They are designed with the idea of having high visibility so they can be readily seen and, being usually fished as wet-flies, depend upon movement rather than form and color for their attraction. The Deceivers are those flies which are patterned after natural insects and, according to Leonard West, "must be a good imitation of an individual species, or sufficiently typical to be at once mistaken for some fly or larva on which the fish are feeding."

The fact that trout take natural flies for food has been overlooked or at least neglected by the fly-fishers in America. There are several reasons for this, and one of the prime reasons is the fact that both of the native trout found in the streams of the eastern part of America, the Rainbow Trout (*Salmo irideus*) and the Char, known to the trout-fisher as the Eastern Brook Trout (*Salvelinus fontinalis*), are by instinct and preference deep feeders and seem to prefer to take their food under water, instead of feeding on the winged insects on the surface of the stream.

With both of these fish, flies of high visibility such as the Royal Coachman, Silver Doctor, Parmachene Belle, etc., fished as deeply-sunk wet-flies, seem to have the desired effect in filling the creel, while the sober-hued flies, more nearly of the coloring of the natural flies found on the stream, fished as dry-flies, seem to be better for the imported Brown Trout.

The Brown Trout will no doubt be the predominant trout in the streams of the East, if it is not already. About 1882 the Brown Trout, or, as they are sometimes erroneously called, the German Brown Trout, were introduced into the American streams. Due to the fact that some of the first eggs of this species of trout were sent over by Herr Von Behr and Herr Von Dem Borne of Germany, the appellation German was attached, while, as a matter of fact, the Brown Trout is the native trout of all Europe and the British Isles as well. Mr. R. B. Marston, editor of the *Fishing Gazette*, London, was one of the first to ship

Brown Trout eggs to this country, and it was through the endeavors of Mr. A. N. Cheney, Fish Culturist for the State of New York, that these fish became firmly established.

It was during this period that Reuben Wood, a prominent American angler, visited England and was greatly surprised that the Brown Trout were so difficult to catch. After trying the typical flies then in use on the American streams, Mr. Wood finally landed one small trout, while anglers who were familiar with the fly then in season took numbers of fine fish. Dry-flies were just coming into their own under the impetus of Halford's FLOATING FLIES AND HOW TO DRESS THEM, and the local English anglers were well armed with good copies of the natural Mayfly on which the trout were feeding.

With the coming of the Brown Trout to American waters, came the necessity for changing the methods of fishing, as these fish did not readily succumb to the Attractor type of fly that was commonly in use for native trout. It was not until the small sober-hued flies of the Deceiver type were fished without drag or manipulation, that these fish were taken in any appreciable quantities.

Around the turn of the present century, our own Theodore Gordon visited England and returned enthusiastic about the dry-fly. No doubt Gordon recognized the value of tying flies suggestive of the natural insect, for the Quill Gordon, which bears his name, is an excellent representation of certain members of the Mayfly family. Gordon's friend, Roy Steenrod, also recognizes the value of representing the natural fly, for the Hendrickson dry-fly, which he designed and named for his friend Mr. A. E. Hendrickson, is a fine copy of a natural fly found throughout the Catskill and Adirondack Mountain districts.

Perhaps the greatest single factor that has deterred the fly-fisher in the study of natural insects found on our streams is the lack of adequate text books covering this field. The reason for this lack is due to the fact that America is a tremendous country, covering a wide range of topographical and climatic conditions, which makes the task of assembling complete information the work of a number of men, each working in a different locality, and as yet no one man has collected a sufficient amount of data to write a book covering the field as a whole.

In this connection Dr. Herman T. Spieth, who has made and still is making an exhaustive study of the family of aquatic flies known as the *Ephemeridae* or Mayflies, tells the writer that at the time of the Glacial Period the northern species of Mayflies were forced to move towards the South, where they intermingled and cross-bred with the Mayflies then occupying that territory, with the resulting confusion which now occurs between closely related species. In Great Britain the condition has been far simpler, as the country is small and there seems to be a correspondingly smaller number of different kinds of flies.

There are several groups of flies which are of interest to the fly-fisher of the streams of the East and these groups are listed below in the order of their importance to him. Nymphs and creepers, found on the bottom of the stream, furnish a large percentage of the food of trout, but these forms are not of great interest to the fly-fisher, unless, of course, the fish are feeding on the Nymphs just as they emerge or hatch. In general, however, the form of insect life with which the dry-fly man is interested is the winged state:

1.	The Mayflies	*Ephemeridae*
2.	The Caddis flies	*Trichoptera*
3.	The Stone flies	*Plecoptera*
4.	The Alder	*Sialidae*
5.	The Black flies	*Diptera*
6.	The Ants	*Hymenoptera*

To date (1935) there is no book in which there is a description of all of these groups of flies, giving the names of the species which occur in America. Louis Rhead, however, published in 1916 his book AMERICAN TROUT STREAM INSECTS, dealing with the natural flies found on the Beaverkill in New York State. Mr. Rhead was an artist and the plates in his book are finely drawn, but the flies depicted are not identified, and as Mr. Rhead named the flies himself, it is impossible to check the species, or even to determine whether the flies are actually different species or only different stages of the same species. Mr. Rhead apparently wanted to control the manufacture of what he called Nature Flies which he designed, and for that reason no dressings of the artificial flies are given in his book. The writer has some of the Rhead flies in his possession and while they are nice to look at, they frankly do not come up to the standards set by the professional fly-tyer of the Catskill regions. Despite the drawbacks of the Rhead flies, the book AMERICAN TROUT STREAM INSECTS has its place in the library of the fly-fisher. This is the only book which deals with the fly life of the American trout streams.

With a longer history of fly-fishing and a simpler assortment of aquatic flies, England is far ahead of us in the matter of books concerning the fly life of their streams. Alfred Ronalds published his delightful book THE FLY-FISHER'S ENTOMOLOGY, as early as 1836, and it is still used as a standard reference work on the trout flies of the British streams. The plates in Ronalds' book show the natural fly as well as the artificial fly in color, and the specifications for dressing the artificial flies are also included.

There is one serious drawback to the use of Ronalds' ENTOMOLOGY as a guide for the study of American stream insects and that is the fact that, without exception, the British flies are of different species from those occurring in America. In a great many cases the same genera of flies will occur in both countries, but the individual species will vary considerably. A second objection to the unqualified use of Ronalds' ENTOMOLOGY is the fact that all of the dressings for the artificial flies are based upon the assumption that the flies were to be fished as wet-flies.

The natural flies depicted in Ronalds' ENTOMOLOGY, however, are more nearly representative of the flies found on the fast rocky streams of the East, than those represented in Halford's DRY FLY ENTOMOLOGY and Mosely's SUPPLEMENT thereto. The reason for this is the fact that Ronalds collected his specimens of natural flies from the streams of the Midlands and the North of England, which streams are similar to ours, while Halford and Mosely were more concerned with the slow-moving chalk streams of the southern part of England, which streams have no counterpart in America unless some of the stillwaters or long pools of the streams in the Adirondacks may be compared. The great difference is the absence of weeds in the Adirondack streams.

Halford's DRY FLY ENTOMOLOGY and Mosely's SUPPLEMENT thereto are therefore of little practical value to the American fly-fisher, except as a means of checking the flies which trout seem to prefer, and trout can be very selective, especially if there happens to be more than one species of natural fly on the water at one time. So much for books dealing with the aquatic flies in general.

In respect to the individual classes of flies there is a little more information available, but most of the language employed is quite technical and a lot of the information has to be predigested and assimilated and the useless discarded. Two extensive books dealing with the *Ephemeridae* or Mayflies have been published, one, Pictet's HISTOIRE NATURELLE DES INSECTES NEUROPTERES, 1843–1845, and the other, Eaton's A REVISIONAL MONOGRAPH OF RECENT EPHEMERIDAE OR MAYFLIES, 1883–1888. Both of these books are, however, very expensive and the first book has the added disadvantage of being published in the French language. There has been a great deal of work done in America on this family of aquatic flies, and it is to be hoped that sometime in the near future a book will be published dealing with the *Ephemeridae* from a scientific point of view. So far most of the observations of the scientists have been confined to the journals of the various Entomological Societies of the United States and Canada, but as yet this information is not in a form for ready consumption by the fly-fisher. The Mayflies are a very important family of flies, both from the standpoint of the fly-fisher and because they furnish a large portion of the trout's food. There is no single class of flies which induces trout to feed on the surface as readily as do the Mayflies.

There is more information available concerning the Caddis flies or *Trichoptera*, as Dr. Cornelius Betten of the New York State Museum has recently published a book on the subject, TRICHOPTERA OF NEW YORK STATE. This book deals with all of the identified species of Caddis flies occurring in New York State, and there is sufficient information given to enable a student of entomology to identify the family and species of almost any Caddis fly found in the East. The Caddis flies are not as important to the fly-fisher as the Mayflies, as most of the Caddis flies emerge or hatch out just at dusk or after dark, when the light is usually so poor that it is difficult or impossible to see a dry-fly on the water. There is no question that these flies in both their creeper and pupal states furnish a great proportion of the trout's diet, but as both of these forms are either crawling around on the bottom of the stream or else are firmly attached to a rock, an imitation of the Caddis worm or pupa is of little value to the fly-fisher. The fly-fisher is most interested in a fish that is either surface-feeding or one that can be induced to surface-feed, and a fish grubbing around the bottom looking for Caddis worms is a pretty poor prospect for him.

Some of the species of small Caddis flies hatch during the early part of the trout-fishing season. A few of these early flies have been noted to emerge during the daylight hours; but, as a general rule, the larger species emerge after dark and many of the big Brown Trout which are caught at night are taken on artificial flies which suggest these large Caddis flies. Some of these flies are valuable contributions to the trout's diet, especially in the early season before the Mayflies have become active.

The Stone flies, or *Plecoptera* of America, have been recently described by Drs. Needham and Claassen of Cornell University in a book called THE PLECOPTERA OF NORTH AMERICA. These flies are not as important as either of the preceding groups of flies, the Mayflies and the Caddis flies, and in addition they are to a large extent carnivorous, living on the nymphs of the Mayflies. The Stone flies seldom emerge from the surface of the stream as do the Mayflies and Caddis flies, but crawl out on some exposed rock or else crawl up on the bank of the stream, where they undergo the change from the creeper to the winged state. Most of the larger species have the disagreeable habit of crawling out during the early hours of the morning, when the fly-fisher is usually in his humble and, to be hoped, virtuous bed. Those species which occur during the first of the open trout-fishing season are sometimes erroneously called Blue Quills and Blue Duns by the local fishermen while, in fact, they are Stone flies and should be called Brown Stone flies or Early Browns to avoid confusing them with the Mayflies which are the true Duns.

The Alder is the only fly of the *Sialidae* group that is of interest to the trout-fisher. The *Corydalis*, or Fish fly, and its creeper, the Helgramite, also belong to this group, but they are of more interest to the bass-fisher and will not be discussed in this book. It might be well in passing to mention the fact that the small creeper found under stones in fast water, and often called the Trout Helgramite, is not a Helgramite at all but is the creeper of one of the Stone flies.

The *Diptera* include the Crane flies and Midges which are to be found around ponds, but their value as models for artificial flies, in the writer's opinion, is nil. The Black Gnats and Smuts also belong to this group, and trout spend a great deal of time in gathering in these tiny flies; for that reason the Black Gnats especially are worth imitating.

Of the family *Hymenoptera*, the Ants are the only insects which get on the water in sufficient quantities to justify being imitated. However, apparently the Bumble Bee occasionally gets on the water, or, at least, large Brown

Trout seem to be familiar with this insect, as a large Western Bee or McGinty wet-fly will often prove the undoing of some wise old Brownie that has resisted the temptations offered by the ordinary patterns of flies. The Bee, like all land flies, should be fished as a wet-fly, as the natural insect, not being accustomed to the water, kicks around and quickly submerges.

For some years past the writer has been collecting natural aquatic flies which occur on the trout streams of the Catskill and Adirondack Mountain regions, and with the kind assistance of friends, to whom his sincere thanks are tendered, a workable collection of flies has been amassed. A collection of flies from a wide geographical range, as well as extending over the best months of the trout-fishing season, is necessary to gain a practical idea as to the distribution of the individual species of flies, as well as their dates of emergence. For instance, a fly that is confined to a single stream, or one that emerges over a short period of time and then disappears until the following season, is not as valuable a fly to imitate as one that has a wide distribution and emerges over a comparatively long period. The common flies are the ones with which the trout are familiar and those are the ones which the writer has segregated.

Identification of the specimens of natural flies was kindly undertaken by Drs. Needham and Betten of Cornell University and Drs. Spieth and Creighton of the College of the City of New York.

By segregating the flies that, because of the frequency of occurrence and wideness of distribution, seemed to be the most common aquatic flies, and checking these specimens with those appearing in Ronalds' ENTOMOLOGY and Halford's DRY FLY ENTOMOLOGY and Mosely's SUPPLEMENT, it has been possible to eliminate certain species which for one reason or another do not seem to appeal to the appetites of the Brown Trout.

Perhaps the most surprising thing that strikes one upon comparing the aquatic flies of America with those found in Great Britain, is the fact that the commonest fly found in England, the one fly that appears on every trout stream from Land's End to Scapa Flow, the Olive Dun, is just about the scarcest fly to be found in America. Out of all the hundreds of flies collected on several streams, one single specimen of the Olive Dun genus (*Baetis*) was found.

Most of the flies found on the fast rocky streams of the North of England have their counterparts on American waters, but as a general rule the American flies run larger in size than those occupying similar positions in the British streams.

Incidentally, most of the flies sold in America have been patterned after natural flies found on the British streams, and, if the truth were known, most of the artificial flies are made by people who have no idea as to what the natural fly which they are imitating looks like. An artificial fly at best is a compromise, and due to the scarcity of good material from which to tie flies, the commercial patterns are usually pretty far removed from the original patterns. If this book does nothing else but call the attention of the angling public to the fact that trout eat natural flies for food, and that they take an artificial fly because of some remote resemblance to the natural fly, it will have served its purpose.

CHAPTER II

THE COLLECTION OF INSECTS

THE collecting of aquatic insects upon which trout feed is a fascinating way of rounding out slack moments on the stream, and in addition adds to the powers of observation.

The writer does not feel that it is necessary to go into the minute differences which distinguish the various species of any one group, but he does feel that it is important to be able to identify the main groups, so that a proper artificial fly may be selected with some degree of intelligence.

There is one thing on which most experienced fly-fishers will agree, and that is the desirability of having confidence in the particular fly or tackle which is being used at the given time, and there is nothing which will give the desired confidence quicker than the knowledge that you have a good representation of the insect on which the trout are feeding.

A magnifying glass of low power is almost a necessity in order to see clearly the marks of identification on some of the smaller flies, such as the *Ephemerella invaria* (Hendrickson), and *Iron pleuralis* (Quill Gordon). An E. Leitz Aplanatic of 6 power magnification is well suited for this purpose.

For those who wish to make a collection of aquatic flies,

the writer would suggest that they obtain a supply of small bottles with screw tops, such as the Economy Capsule Bottle, No. 112, made by the Whitall Tatum Company of New York City. These bottles are strong and will stand a lot of abuse. They should be well filled with collecting fluid, as the flies are very delicate in structure and will be broken into bits by sloshing around in a bottle half filled with fluid. These bottles should also be equipped with labels so that the date and stream may be noted thereon, as specimens without this attending information are of little value.

Where it is not necessary to preserve the color, plain grain alcohol of seventy per cent strength is an ideal preserving fluid and is the one commonly used by most scientists. The delicate shades of color, however, fade rapidly in alcohol unless about five per cent of acetic acid is added to the solution. This acid tends to set the color and to some extent prevents fading; about five per cent glycerine and five per cent benzol, if added, will tend to keep the specimen soft and reduce the chances of breakage.

In cases where the insect is to be used as a model for copying it is desirable to have as fresh a specimen as possible, for there is bound to be some discoloration or fading as time goes on.

Flies are difficult to capture, especially when they are emerging from fast flowing water, and for that reason the writer prefers to keep a close watch on back-waters and eddies where emerging flies may often be picked up with a minimum of fuss. The Mayflies are so delicate that they are often crushed when captured, and if it is possible to get them in a still pool or gently flowing eddy they may be picked up by the wings and put into the bottle of fluid without injury to their structure.

Scientists collecting the Mayflies usually carry a long-handled net, but the fly-fisher is already so burdened with tackle that it is not suggested that he too carry a net. The fly-fisher, however, is concerned with the Subimagos or Duns, which are comparatively slow in flight, while the scientist is concerned with the Imago or Spinner which is very active. The entomologist prefers to collect the Spinners or Imagos for the reason that the wing veins, which are used to determine the species, stand out more sharply in the Spinner than in the Subimago or Dun. They also are especially interested in the male Imagos for the reason that the male genitalia are sometimes used as a determining factor in identifying the species.

Aquatic flies are very suspicious of any moving object and will avoid coming near as long as there is any movement to frighten them, but if you remain motionless, often the egg-laying Spinners will come near enough to permit catching them in your hat. Most of the Mayflies deposit their eggs in gravelly runs and those are the places to watch for the egg-laying Spinners, especially late in the afternoon.

Entomologists do not put much faith in color as a means of determining the species of insects, as the shade of color of any fly is so changeable and evasive that it is not dependable as a means of identification. The habitat of a fly may control the color characteristic; for instance, flies from exposed areas in a stream may be considerably lighter in coloring than specimens of the same fly taken from the shaded and woody portions of the same stream, although there is no scientific verification of this.

The dates of emergence of any particular species as given in the following pages are not to be taken as the definite dates upon which the species *will appear* on certain streams. They are, however, the actual dates upon which specimens of the natural flies *were* collected from the streams.

The exact date of emergence of any species seems to be governed by water temperatures, and seasons when there is a lot of cloudy weather the appearance of a certain species of fly may be delayed beyond its customary emergence date.

PART II

ARTIFICIAL MAYFLIES AND VARIANTS

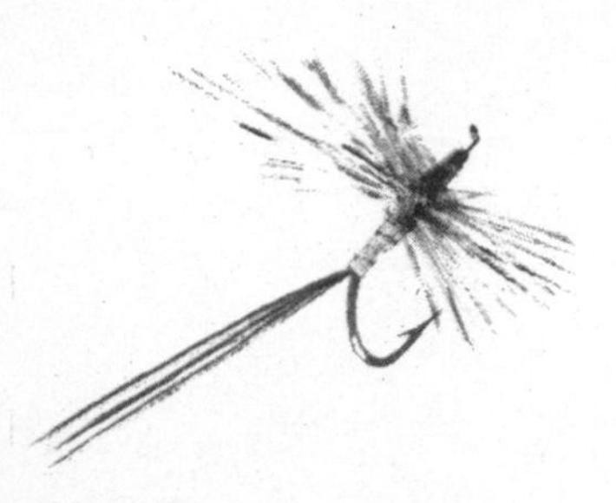

1. Green Drake

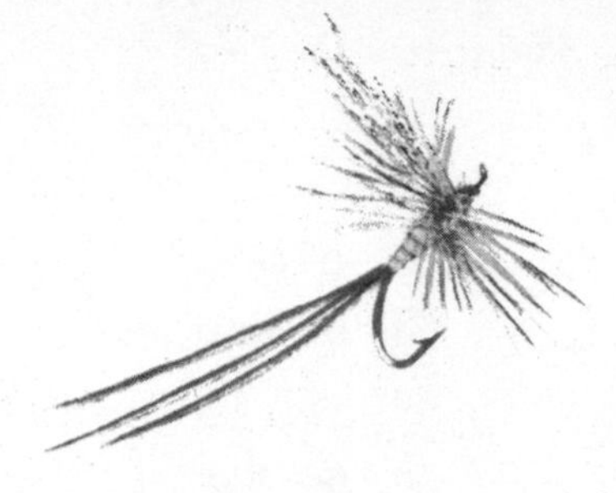

2. Coffin Fly

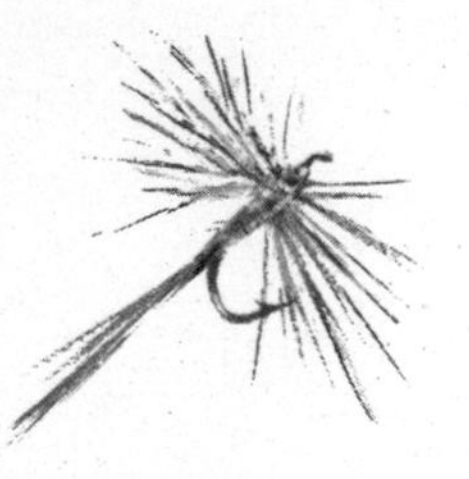

3. Gold Bodied Variant

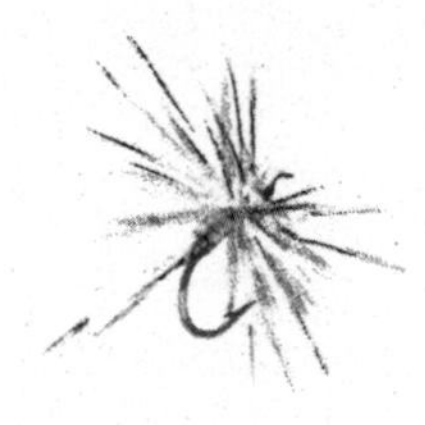

4. Cream Variant

5. Royal Coachman

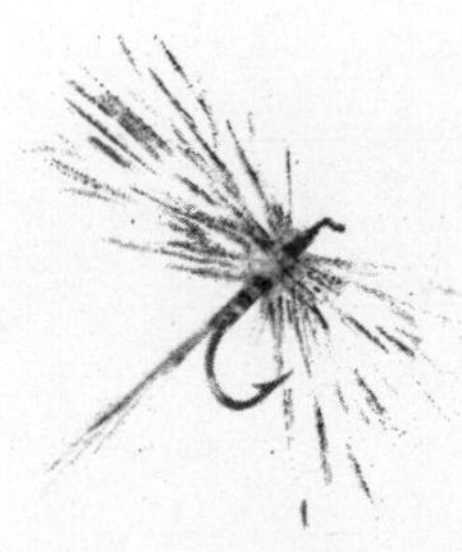

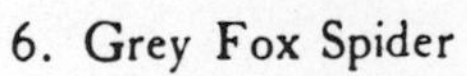

6. Grey Fox Spider

CHAPTER I

Ephemeridae

All the Mayflies or Drakes are called the *Ephemeridae* because of the shortness of their lives in the winged state, their existence as true flies being limited to a few days at most.

Before the transformation into a winged fly, these insects live in the stream as Nymphs, and this stage of their life may cover a period ranging from a few months to three years.

The Mayflies are of particular interest to the fly-fisher for the reason that they are water-bred flies, furnishing in both their nymphal and winged states much-appreciated food for the trout.

The transformation from the nymphal stage to the winged stage takes place upon the surface of the stream, which process is usually referred to by the fly-fisher as "hatching." At this time the flies are known as Duns, for the reason that their wings have a smoky dull appearance. The fly immediately after hatching is known to the scientist as a Subimago, but to the fly-fisher it is a Dun; incidentally this applies to all of the flies of this group, big or little.

Trout feed on the Nymphs as they ascend to the surface of the stream to emerge or hatch, and in that way become acquainted with the winged fly. On the fast streams of the East more flies are consumed in the Dun stage than in the final or Spinner stage, the reason being that the trout have been induced to rise in following the ascending Nymphs.

The females after mating return to the stream to deposit the fertile eggs, and trout again have an opportunity of feeding on these flies as, in many species, the female dips to the water to wash off the eggs. In this, the final state, both male and female are known as Spinners, because of the erratic movements during flight. Scientifically they are known as Imagos.

As this family of flies is most generally imitated in artificial trout flies, a general description of the class is given as follows:

Head—Usually small, the mouth parts being atrophied and useless for taking food.

Eyes—The eyes are compound, and the eyes of the male are larger and more brilliantly colored.

Thorax—The thorax is thick and heavy, furnishing the muscular power to drive the wings, which are attached.

Legs—The legs are in three pairs, attached to the thorax.

Wings—The wings consist of two pairs of membranes, the forward pair large and spreading, the hind wings small and in some cases absent. When at rest the wings are held erect over the body, giving rise to the name Upwing.

Body—The body is long and soft, being composed of 10 segments or joints; attached to the hinder end are two, sometimes three tails.

Forceps—The males are equipped with a pair of forceps attached to the ninth segment of their bodies. These are a ready means of identifying males.

Tails—The tails consist of two or three many jointed filaments or hairs.

The life cycle is as follows: The fertile eggs are always deposited in the water by the female. Often this is accomplished by the insect dipping to the surface of the stream where the eggs are washed off by the force of the running water. Some types, of which *Ephemerella* is an example, drop their eggs as packets or balls while flying over the water. The eggs, having been deposited, sink to the bottom of the stream where the change from the egg to the Nymph takes place. The time required for the Nymph to grow to a mature fly varies in accordance with the species of the fly, some taking possibly as long as three years. Generally, larger species take the longest time.

The young Nymph either hides among the gravel and stones or vegetation of the stream bottom, or burrows into the silt. Some of the early writers on the subject of entomology, notably Pictet, classified the Nymphs in accordance with their habitat and method of locomotion, such as Burrowers, Clamberers, Swimmers, etc.

The Nymph consumes large quantities of vegetable matter, and as it grows and expands it becomes necessary to shed its skin and grow a new and larger one, this process being repeated many times during the life of the Nymph; in fact, some twenty molts have been noted during the life of one specimen in a laboratory.

The Nymph resembles the mature fly to some extent, except that the Nymph has no wings. The wing cases or covers, however, are present, and the approximate date of the emergence or hatch can be predicted by the development of these wing covers.

The Nymph has a good appetite, as during the nymphal period a sufficient amount of energy has to be stored to take care of the fly's existence in the winged state as well. The mouth parts are particularly well developed; in fact, the mouth is so prominent that some authorities considered the Mayfly Nymphs as being carnivorous, but it has been fairly well established that they are primarily vegetarians. The thorax is well developed, and supports the three pairs of legs. The body of the Nymph, like that of the mature fly, is composed of ten segments and attached to the first seven segments are seven pairs of gills which are used to extract oxygen from the water. The Stone fly creepers, which are sometimes confused with the Nymphs of the Mayflies, carry their gills on their thorax. Attached to the last segment of the Mayfly body are three (sometimes two) tails; these tails are short in comparison with the length of the tails in the mature fly. The Nymph usually has three tails, while the mature fly may have three tails or, in many instances, only two.

In describing the Nymphs of the Mayflies it might be well to point out again that the gills are carried on the first seven segments of the body or abdomen, while the gills of the Stone fly creeper are carried on the thorax. A further means of distinguishing between these two common insects is the fact that the Mayfly Nymphs have a single claw on each foot, while the creeper of the Stone fly has two claws on each foot. The Nymphs of the Dragon flies and the Damsel flies are too large to be easily confused with the Mayflies, and the Helgramite is a common friend of all stream fishermen. The Nymph of the Alder burrows deep into the stream-bed and is seldom seen either by a fish or a fisherman.

As the Nymph approaches the time when the transformation into a winged fly is about to take place, it becomes very restless, swimming about and generally showing much activity. Specimens in tanks have been observed to make several trips to and from the surface before finally breaking the nymphal shuck and emerging as winged flies. It is during this period, just prior to a general hatch of any one species, that the trout gorge themselves on the ascending Nymph. The Nymph is apparently so engrossed in its own efforts to undergo the transformation to the winged state, that it seems to cast its usual caution to the winds.

The nymphal shuck is cast off by the Nymph splitting the shuck between the shoulders, this operation being assisted to some extent by the formation of a gas within the nymphal shuck. The wings are promptly unfurled to dry; in the meantime the cast-off shuck is used as a raft and is carried along by the current. As soon as the wings are dried, which takes only a few seconds, the fly, known as a Subimago or Dun, flutters upward to some nearby tree or wall where it alights to spend the succeeding twenty-four hours in undergoing a still further molt of another complete skin. In the stage in which they are known as Duns the flies are rather poor flyers and fall easy prey to any passing bird. They are easy to collect and show little inclination to escape by flight. The final molt takes from twelve to twenty-four hours depending upon the species, but the flies that are of interest to the fly-fisher take twenty-four hours.

In the Subimago or Dun stage, both the males and females of the same species have the same general appearance, and the writer does not feel that there is anything to be gained by trying to differentiate between them as far as the artificial fly is concerned, except in a few cases where the flies occur in such numbers that the fish become very selective.

In the final stage, the Imago or Spinner shows considerable difference between the sexes. Trout in our fast streams do not seem to feed on the Spinners, but if anyone wishes to copy a Spinner the writer would suggest that the female be selected, as she has to return to the stream to lay her eggs while the male may or may not return to the stream to die.

Once, while talking over the fishing conditions with a local Catskill fisherman who, by the way, is an expert at getting fish, he remarked that he had been fishing the previous day but had caught nothing. He was then asked about natural flies and the answer was to the effect that there were lots of flies but it was only a "brush hatch." All of the flies seemed to be hatching out in the woods and none hatching out of the water. Of course, the fact of the matter was that the females, having molted, were returning to the stream to mate and lay eggs.

The Mayflies do not take any food while in their winged states, their mouth parts being entirely atrophied. All of the eating has been done in the previous or nymphal stage.

Immediately after the final molt when the fly becomes an Imago or Spinner, the dull listlessness which characterizes the Subimago or Dun disappears and the fly becomes exceedingly active, dancing and darting through the air with express speed, bent upon the culminating event of its ephemeral life, namely, to procreate and die.

Actual mating takes place in the air, the male approaching the female from below, where, with the aid of the forceps and the elongated front legs, he clings until the eggs are fertilized; flight is maintained by the female during this process.

After the eggs have been fertilized by the male the female returns to the stream to deposit her eggs and fall spent upon the surface in a dying condition. In this condition the fly is known as a Spent Spinner or a Spent Gnat.

The eggs are extruded between the seventh and eighth body segments and some species, as is the case with the *Ephemerella* previously referred to, hover over the water with their eggs partly extruded. Artificial flies are often made with a green or yellow egg sac, which is to represent the eggs so carried. Apparently fish are accustomed to feeding on flies which spend a goodly period of time in voiding their eggs, as the Female Beaverkill, a wet-fly probably patterned after the *Ephemerella invaria*, is a very effective fly in attracting the trout of the Catskill regions and the Beaverkill stream in particular.

Male Spinners are not of much use as models for trout flies as so many of these flies never return to the stream. They, however, live longer than the females and often a few of them will be found around some time after the females have disappeared. The males are slightly smaller than the females, and Halford used some of them on that account; but on our waters there is no necessity for making such fine distinctions.

In order that there be no confusion, the following points of difference between the sexes can be distinguished without the aid of a microscope: Male Spinners have tails longer than their bodies and the forelegs are usually much elongated. The eyes are larger and brighter than the females' and, finally, the presence or absence of the forceps is a conclusive characteristic.

The patterns of artificial flies referred to in the following pages are not to be considered the *only* flies which will take fish under any given condition, but they have been selected by the writer as being *sufficiently near the natural fly in size and coloring* to take fish when they are definitely feeding on the corresponding natural fly.

NATURAL DUNS

1. *Acentrella* (Iron Blue Dun)

2. *Blasturus* (See text)

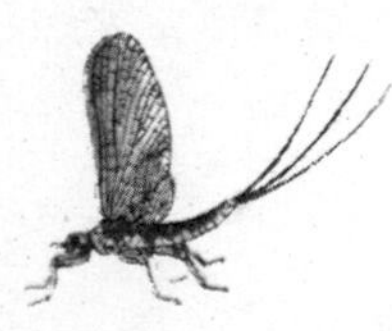

4. *Ephemerella invaria*
female Spinner with eggs

3. *Ephemerella invaria*
female Dun (Hendrickson)

5. *Ephemerella invaria*
male Dun (Red Quill)

8. *Iron* (*Epeorus*) male Dun
(Dark Quill Gordon)

6. *Iron* (*Epeorus*)
female Dun (Quill Gordon)

7. Middle leg of *Iron* (*Epeorus*)

CHAPTER II

EPHEMERELLA INVARIA WALKER

HENDRICKSON

EPHEMERELLA INVARIA is the scientific name for a Mayfly, the female of which is represented by that popular dry-fly, the Hendrickson.

There are several flies belonging to this group, including *Ephemerella subvaria* and *Ephemerella rotunda*, but for all practical purposes *Ephemerella invaria* may be taken as a type.

These flies are widely distributed and seem to enjoy the quiet slow-moving streams as well as the fast rocky streams. They emerge over a fairly wide range and specimens have been collected as early as April 21st on the Paulinskill at Blairstown, N. J., and as late as June 12th on the Ausable at Wilmington, N. Y. The main hatch, however, usually occurs during the middle of May in the Catskill regions and the latter part of May in the Adirondacks.

Ephemerella invaria is slightly larger than *Epeorus* (Quill Gordon) with which it often emerges, but *Ephemerella* may be identified by the fact that it has three tails, and the tails are segmented with brown markings at the joints. The brown speckles or markings may be easily seen with the aid of a low-power magnifying glass.

The measurements are as follows: Subimago or Dun,

Female	Wing—½ inch
	Body—⅜ inch
	Tails—⅜ inch
Male	Wing—⅜ inch
	Body—5/16 inch
	Tails—7/16 inch

The female Subimago or Dun is well represented by the dry-fly known as the Hendrickson. This dry-fly was first designed in 1916 by Roy Steenrod of Liberty, N. Y., and while it was patterned after the natural *Ephemerella invaria*, Roy did not know the scientific name for the fly, so he named it the Hendrickson in honor of Mr. A. E. Hendrickson, a well-known sportsman and fly-fisher. The dressing of the original Hendrickson dry-fly is as follows:

Wings—Flank feather of male wood-duck
Body—Fawn colored fur from belly of a red fox
Legs—Rusty dun cock hackle
Tail—Few strands of wood-duck flank feather
Silk—Yellow
Hook—No. 10 Hardy

Mandarin may be substituted for the wood-duck flank feather and a few strands of cock hackle used for the tails, without detracting from the killing qualities of this fly.

The males are slightly smaller and for that reason are sometimes referred to by the fly-fisher as "Little Hendricksons;" their bodies being of a decidedly ruddy color they are better represented by an artificial fly known in the Catskill regions as the Red Quill, the dressing of which is as follows:

Wings—Flank feather of male mandarin duck
Body—Quill, stripped large hackle feather from a red cock
Legs—Dark rusty dun cock
Tail—Dark rusty dun cock hackle barbs
Hook—No. 11 Hardy

Owing to the importance of this family of flies and also due to the fact that the males emerge from the stream at a different time from the females, it is suggested that copies of both sexes be carried in the fly-box.

When the *Ephemerella* flies are ready to deposit their eggs, both males and females fly upstream, and they may then be recognized by the fact that the female carries her eggs partially extruded from her body. The egg mass is oval in shape; it is of a bright lemon yellow color.

The eggs are dropped while the female is flying over gravelly riffles and it is seldom that the fly actually drops to the surface to deposit the eggs, apparently dropping them while flying at a short distance above the surface. Mention is made of this as so many fancy patterns of dry-flies are tied with egg-sacs, but for all practical purposes they may as well be omitted since the fish do not get a chance to reach the natural fly while she is carrying the eggs.

The wet-fly known as the Lady or Female Beaverkill is probably taken by the trout as a crippled Subimago or Dun whose eggs have been crushed out of the body, rather than an Imago or Spinner of the *Ephemerella* either carrying her eggs or depositing eggs. This conjecture is somewhat borne out by the fact that the Lady Beaverkill has never in the writer's experience been particularly successful when fished as a dry-fly.

Dr. McDunnough, of the Entomological branch of the Canadian Government, made a special study of the genus *Ephemerella*, and some of his observations have appeared from time to time in the *Journal of the Canadian Entomological Society*. As this fly is one of the most important in the fly-fisher's kit, the writer begs the indulgence of the reader and quotes the following from Dr. McDunnough's observations:

"The Nymphs frequent the swifter parts of the stream and are most frequently met with along the banks among grass and refuse. They are all distinctly inhabitants of swift water and occur under rocks or submerged pieces of wood, frequently at considerable depth and in places where the current is full of silt.

"The color of the males (Imagos or Spinners) is a brown of varying shades but generally with a decided ruddy tinge, the females being paler and tending towards yellow or ochreous—the legs are bright yellow, and the setae (tails), with one exception, are distinctly banded with brown." [NOTE: Words in parentheses are the author's.]

It has been the writer's experience that when trout are feeding on the *Ephemerella* fly, they are very selective and will even refuse a well-tied Quill Gordon which, incidentally, is similar in appearance to the Hendrickson, except for the body. If the natural flies, *Ephemerella* and *Iron* (*Epeorus*), be compared it will be found that the body of the *Ephemerella* is much thicker especially at the thorax; also the distinct markings which characterize the body of the *Iron* (*Epeorus*) are absent, and apparently the trout have no difficulty in distinguishing between the two flies.

Some years ago when the dry-fly was first becoming popular in America, the fancy pattern known as the Whirling Dun was considered one of, if not the most popular fly, but in recent years the Whirling Dun has been supplanted by the Hendrickson. Both flies are probably taken by the trout as representing members of the genus *Ephemerella*, but the Hendrickson dry-fly has the advantage of being made of materials which will wear much better than the starling or duck quill-feather wing of the Whirling Dun.

The genus *Ephemerella* is represented in the British Isles by *Ephemerella ignita*, the famous Blue-winged Olive of the South Country chalk streams.

EMERGENCE DATES

Ephemerella invaria

Stream	City and State	Date
Paulinskill	Blairstown, New Jersey	April 21, 1934
So. Branch Raritan	Califon, New Jersey	April 29, 1934
Esopus	Mount Tremper, New York	May 5, 1934

Stream	City and State	Date
Schoharie	Lexington, New York	May 19, 1934
Beaverkill	Roscoe, New York	May 20, 1934
East Branch Delaware	Margaretville, New York	May 21, 1934
West Branch Ausable	Wilmington, New York	May 26, 1934
Esopus	Mount Tremper, New York	June 6, 1934
Brodhead	Analomink, Pennsylvania	April 24, 1935
Brodhead	Analomink, Pennsylvania	April 26, 1935
Brodhead	Analomink, Pennsylvania	April 27, 1935
Brodhead	Analomink, Pennsylvania	April 28, 1935
Brodhead	Analomink, Pennsylvania	April 29, 1935
Mongaup	Monticello, New York	April 28, 1935
Esopus	Mount Tremper, New York	May 4, 1935
Beaverkill	Beaverkill, New York	May 11, 1935
Beaverkill	Cook's Falls, New York	May 12, 1935
Beaverkill	Peaksville, New York	May 18, 1935
West Branch Ausable	Wilmington, New York	June 1–12, 1935 (inclusive)

CHAPTER III

Ephemerella dorothea Needham

Pale Evening Dun

Ephemerella dorothea Needham is the scientific name for the small yellow Mayfly which emerges just at dark during the month of June. It is the nearest thing that the writer has been able to find to correspond to what is called, in England, the Pale Evening Dun or the Pale Watery Dun.

It is a small fly with three tails, but the characteristic marking of the *Ephemerella*, brown markings at the joints, is absent. The measurements are as follows:

Wing—¼ inch
Body—¼ inch
Tails—¼ inch

Specimens have been collected from the Paulinskill at Blairstown, N. J., on June 2, 1934, and from the West Branch of the Ausable at Wilmington, N. Y., on June 23, 1934.

This fly is well represented by the Little Marryat, the dressing of which is as follows:

Wings—Palest starling
Body—Fur from the flank of an Australian opossum

Legs—Pale ginger cock
Tails—Ginger cock barbs
Silk—Primrose
Hook—No. 14 Hardy

The natural fly after which the Little Marryat was patterned does not occur on our streams.

These small flies are difficult to see, especially when it is rapidly getting dark and the writer prefers a large fly of the Variant type for use at this time of the day as it can be seen.

CHAPTER IV

Iron (Epeorus) pleuralis Banks

Quill Gordon

Iron (Epeorus) pleuralis Banks is the scientific name of the medium-sized Mayfly which occurs early in the trout-fishing season and which is often referred to by the fly-fisher as a "Quill."

When Dr. Eaton wrote his monograph on Mayflies, he described a genus occurring in Europe, which he designated as *Epeorus;* a somewhat similar type occurring in America he designated as *Iron.* The species described as *pleuralis Banks* has been put in both genera at various times, hence the name *Iron* (*Epeorus*).

The pronounced body markings, the alternate bands of light and dark, are well represented by a piece of quill stripped from the peacock's shoulder feather.

There is considerable variation in the shade of coloring of this fly and specimens from the Brodhead in Pennsylvania are quite light, giving rise to the name of Yellow Quill by which the fly is known to native fishermen on that stream.

While the writer has no positive proof that *Iron* (*Epeorus*) is the natural fly which Theodore Gordon copied when he designed his famous Quill Gordon, he is perfectly well satisfied that a well-tied Quill Gordon will be taken by the trout for this natural fly. The natural is very plentiful on such streams as provide a suitable habitat for it, and the fish are inclined to be very picky when the fly is emerging; in fact, a Quill Gordon tied with a light dun hackle is about the only fly which is taken with confidence.

The natural fly is widely distributed, but seems to be confined to streams which are relatively free from pollution. It appears to be particularly plentiful on the Brodhead in Pennsylvania, and on the Beaverkill at the town of Beaverkill, N. Y. It is not meant to convey the idea that streams which do not have this fly in good numbers must be highly polluted, there may be other reasons; but so far, the fly has been limited to spring-fed streams which are free from pollution.

Ephemerella invaria (Hendrickson) is often found emerging at the same time as *Iron* (*Epeorus*), but the *Ephemerella invaria* seems to enjoy a lot of streams on which *Iron* (*Epeorus*) is not found. In cases where the two flies are emerging at the same time, the fish may be taking one species to the entire exclusion of the other, so it is a good idea to try both artificial flies over a good fish before passing it by. As a rule the Quill Gordon will take fish when they are feeding on *Iron* (*Epeorus*).

The female is slightly larger than the male and is slightly paler in coloring; the actual measurements are as follows:

IRON (EPEORUS) PLEURALIS BANKS

Subimago or Dun

Female	Male
Wing—7/16 inch	Wing—3/8 inch
Body—3/8 inch	Body—5/16 inch
Tail—1/2 inch	Tail—3/8 inch

As this is one of the most important flies in the fly-fisher's book of flies, it is recommended that both the male and female be represented, for when fly life is so abundant the trout gorge themselves with food and sometimes become very selective.

The dressings of the artificials are as follows:

Quill Gordon

Wings—Mandarin flank feather
Body—Peacock quill, light
Rib—Fine gold wire
Legs—Light blue dun game cock
Tail—Few light blue dun cock barbs
Hook—No. 10 Hardy

The above dressing represents the female fly, and the dressing to suggest the male should be the same as above, except darker throughout and the hook should be a No. 11 Hardy.

In the Adirondacks, occupying a similar position in the stream, is a fly of the same general appearance as *Epeorus;* however, the scientific name is *Rithrogena* and it will be referred to under that name.

Iron (*Epeorus*) is a dark fly, having smoky blue wings. The tails are two in number, and the identifying characteristics are the brown marks upon the legs. These marks will be found on what corresponds to the thigh, and also at the joints or knees.

Iron (*Epeorus*) does not occur in England, but the writer is informed that a well-tied Quill Gordon will take fish there just the same. The natural of the genus *Epeorus* does occur in Europe.

EMERGENCE DATES

Iron (*Epeorus*) *pleuralis Banks*

STREAM	CITY AND STATE	DATE
Schoharie	Lexington, New York	May 19, 1934
Esopus	Mount Tremper, New York	June 9, 1934
Brodhead	Analomink, Pennsylvania	April 20, 1935
Brodhead	Analomink, Pennsylvania	April 24, 1935
Brodhead	Analomink, Pennsylvania	April 26, 1935
Brodhead	Analomink, Pennsylvania	April 27, 1935
Brodhead	Analomink, Pennsylvania	April 28, 1935
Esopus	Mount Tremper, New York	April 27, 1935
Esopus	Mount Tremper, New York	May 4, 1935
Beaverkill	Beaverkill, New York	May 6, 1935
Beaverkill	Beaverkill, New York	May 16, 1935
Beaverkill	Beaverkill, New York	May 18, 1935
Beaverkill	Beaverkill, New York	May 19, 1935

CHAPTER V

Rithrogena impersonata McDunnough
Quill Gordon

On May 26, 1934, there was a heavy hatch of dark winged Mayflies on the West Branch of the Ausable River near Wilmington, N. Y., and as there had been excellent sport with the Hendrickson dry-fly the day previous, when the *Ephemerella invaria* was on the water, the writer was disappointed when rising fish refused to have anything to do with a Hendrickson fly.

Specimens of the flies were secured, and as they had the characteristic markings on their legs which indicate *Iron* (*Epeorus*), the fly which is represented by the Quill Gordon, a Quill Gordon dry-fly was substituted for the Hendrickson, and four heavy fish were then taken in rapid succession. Other members of the party then switched to Quill Gordons and also took fish.

Specimens of the natural fly were sent to Dr. Needham for identification, and he pronounced it a member of the genus *Rithrogena*, only two species having been reported from the eastern part of the United States. As only females had been collected, it was not possible to determine the exact species. Males, however, were secured on June 3, 1935, from the same locality, and these have been identified as *Rithrogena impersonata McDunnough* by Dr. Spieth.

As far as the writer is able to ascertain, this fly is limited to the West Branch of the Ausable, but as it so closely resembles the fly which we have in the Catskill regions, known as *Iron (Epeorus) pleuralis Banks*, the interest is only academic, since a Quill Gordon will take fish when this fly is on the water, and that is what the fly-fisher wishes to know.

STENONEMA GROUP

1. *Stenonema vicarium* Dun (American March Brown)

2. *Stenonema fuscum* Dun (Grey Fox)

3. *Stenonema ithaca* Dun (Light Cahill)

4. Middle leg of *Stenonema* group

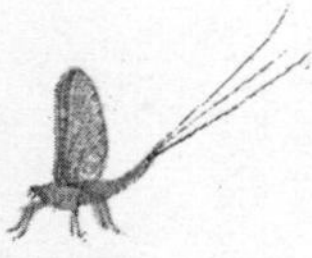

5. *Ephemerella dorothea* Dun (Little Marryat)

6. *Sialis infumata* (American Alder)

CHAPTER VI

Stenonema Group
American March Brown
Grey Fox
Light Cahill

STENONEMA is the scientific name which has been given to a group of Mayflies. It is the generic name and the different members of the genus are distinguished by additional names denoting the species.

The grouping of some twenty species under the family name of *Stenonema* is of recent date; in fact, the name first appeared in the June, 1933, issue of the *Journal of the New York Entomological Society*. Dr. Jay R. Traver constructed the genus for those American species that had formerly been placed in the genus *Ecdyonurus*. The name "*stenonema*" is descriptive of the threadlike seventh gill of the Nymph.

While there are twenty species of Mayflies assigned to this group, a great many of them emerge from the stream after dark and for that reason are of little direct interest to the fly-fisher. There are four flies of this group which are of interest and as two of them are so much alike they will be treated as a single fly.

As the Nymphs emerge as Subimagos or Duns they usually are rather slow in getting off the water; in fact, the Duns often make several efforts to take wing, fluttering a few feet at a time with rather bumpy landings on the surface of the stream. This movement on the surface of course attracts the attention of any fish in the immediate vicinity. This one characteristic endears them to the heart of the fly-fisher.

STENONEMA VICARIUM
AMERICAN MARCH BROWN

The first member of this group to arrive in the spring is *Stenonema vicarium* or the American March Brown. This is a large fly with mottled brownish wings slanting back at an angle of about sixty degrees. This is the best way of identifying the March Brown, as none of the other flies of this group has the wings slanted at quite such an acute angle. Like all Mayflies the size may vary a little in accordance with the amount of food available, but average specimens will measure as follows:

	Stenonema vicarium
Female	Wing—5/8 inch
Subimago or Dun	Body—9/16 inch
	Tails—1/2 inch

As far as the writer is aware there has been no good dry-fly dressing for this fly, as the British March Brown dry-flies are generally tied with a soft partridge hackle and wings of pheasant, both feathers being too soft for the type of fly useful on our fast streams. The following dressing is the writer's choice for this fly, and in practice has been successful:

American March Brown

Wings—Flank feather of mallard drake
Body—Red fox belly mixed with sandy fur from a hare's poll
Hackle—Bright red game cock, with a grey grizzle cock's hackle worked in as the front hackle
Tail—Red game cock's barbs
Hook—No. 9 Hardy
Silk—Orange

The March Brown occurs in the Catskills as early as May 20th and ranges up through the Adirondacks where it is plentiful during the first two weeks in June.

STENONEMA FUSCUM
GREY FOX

The next fly of this group is called *Stenonema fuscum.* It is also a large fly, with mottled wings, but is considerably lighter in coloring than the March Brown. The wings also slant back but not at such an acute angle as the fly described above. The natural fly is well represented by an artificial fly which the writer designed some years ago, and which for want of a better name has been called the Grey Fox. There have been many flies to which this name has been given at various times, so in order to avoid confusion the dressing of the Grey Fox referred to is given as follows:

Grey Fox

Wings—Flank feather of a mallard drake
Body—Light red fur from red fox belly
Hackle—Ginger game, with light grizzled cock's hackle worked in as the front hackle
Tail—Ginger game cock's barbs
Hook—No. 10 Hardy
Silk—Primrose

This fly is about the same size as the March Brown; if anything slightly smaller. It usually follows the March Brown in emerging, but frequently both flies will emerge at the same time, and both flies seem to be equally attractive to the fish.

STENONEMA ITHACA & CANADENSIS
LIGHT CAHILL

Following the Grey Fox, *Stenonema fuscum*, will be found two pale yellow flies with mottled wings, these being *Stenonema ithaca* and *Stenonema canadensis*. These flies usually are in evidence during the second half of June in the Catskill regions and have been found on June 23rd in the Adirondacks. There are usually several species of pale yellow Mayflies in evidence at this season of the year, but for some reason the *Stenonema* flies seem to be particularly attractive to the fish. For all practical purposes the measurements of only one of these flies will be given as follows:

Stenonema ithaca

Female	Wing—5/16 inch
Subimago or Dun	Body—3/8 inch
	Tails—3/8 inch

This fly is well represented by the pattern of dry-fly known as the Light Cahill. The first record of the Cahill fly which the writer has been able to find, is in the small book entitled THE ART OF ANGLING, by Holberton, published in 1887. Marbury, in 1892, lists the Cahill, and attributes it to the hand of a Dublin fly-maker, whose flies were so lifelike that he would hold them to his ear to see if they would buzz. The early Cahill was a dark fly, with a body of muskrat and a dark red hackle for legs, but as time went on it was gradually lightened, first by Theodore Gordon, who used a sandy fur body and a light red hackle, and finally by William Chandler of Neversink, N. Y., who is responsible for the current dressing which is given as follows:

Light Cahill

Wings—Flank feather from a mandarin drake
Body—Light fur from the belly of a red fox
Legs—Light ginger cock's hackle
Tail—Light ginger cock's barbs
Hook—No. 11 Hardy
Silk—Primrose

There is one characteristic which will enable the fly-fisher to identify the *Stenonema* flies on the stream, and that is the markings on the legs. All of the flies described above have barred markings on what might be called their thighs; this coupled with the mottled wings makes their identification fairly simple.

The Nymphs of these flies are of the flattened type, well suited for living under stones or clinging to stones. They spend a great part of their lives in fast water but appear to migrate to the little pools and placid spots adjacent to fast water as they mature.

The Nymph of the March Brown makes a good general pattern of wet-fly for use in the riffles or when the water is roiled. The dressing for the Nymph is as follows:

Body—Red fox belly fur mixed with the sandy fur from a hare's poll
Legs—Light red cock's hackle, soft
Tails—Three strands of a cock pheasant's tail
Hook—No. 8 Hardy or No. 6 Bartlett B 7362
Silk—Orange

Note: A bunched mandarin flank feather should be tied flat over the back, to suggest the darker portion of the Nymph's body.

Later in the season when the Grey Fox, *Stenonema fuscum*, is in evidence, a Light Cahill wet-fly tied on a No. 8 Hardy hook is an excellent wet-fly to use in place of the March Brown Nymph. The dressing is the same as for the dry-fly, but the tying of the fly should be done in a manner suggestive of the Nymph.

There are several other species of the *Stenonema* group in the writer's collection of flies from trout streams, but as they are all small pale yellow flies that emerge after dark, their value to the fly-fisher is questionable.

EMERGENCE DATES

Stenonema vicarium

Stream	City and State	Date
Neversink	Bradley, New York	May 25, 1933
Esopus	Mount Tremper, New York	June 9, 1934
West Branch Ausable	Wilmington, New York	June 23, 1934
Ausable	Wilmington, New York	June 7, 1935
Ausable	Wilmington, New York	June 11, 1935
East Branch Ausable	Upper Jay, New York	June 12, 1935
Chazy	Ellenburg, New York	June 8, 1935

Stenonema fuscum

Stream	City and State	Date
Beaverkill	Roscoe, New York	May 20, 1934
East Branch Delaware	Margaretville, New York	May 21, 1934
Esopus	Mount Tremper, New York	June 4, 1934
Esopus	Mount Tremper, New York	June 9, 1934
Chazy	Ellenburg, New York	June 8, 1935
East Branch Ausable	Upper Jay, New York	June 9, 1935

Stream	City and State	Date
West Branch Ausable	Wilmington, New York	June 6, 1935
Ausable	Wilmington, New York	June 10, 1935
Ausable	Wilmington, New York	June 14, 1935

Stenonema ithaca
Stenonema canadensis

Stream	City and State	Date
Esopus	Mount Tremper, New York	June 30, 1933
Neversink	Bradley, New York	June 10, 1934
West Branch Ausable	Wilmington, New York	June 23, 1934
Esopus	Mount Tremper, New York	June 15, 1935

CHAPTER VII

ISONYCHIA BICOLOR WALKER

LEADWING COACHMAN

THERE are several members of the *Isonychia* group of Mayflies, but the one with which the fly-fisher is concerned is *Isonychia bicolor Walker*.

Isonychia bicolor is a large dark fly with a ruddy body and dark grey, almost black wings; the legs are of different colors, hence the name bicolor. The middle and hind pairs of legs are a bright yellow while the forelegs are reddish brown of about the same color as the body.

The male Imagos or Spinners have a clear ruby colored body, which looks like a red hot spark in the air, the wings being transparent and colorless.

Isonychia is a large fly, measurements of the female Subimago or Dun being as follows:

Wing—11/16 inch
Body—5/8 inch
Tails—7/16 inch

This fly has one characteristic which makes identification fairly easy: it holds its forelegs, when at rest, out in front of the body as though it desired to shake hands. It is the only Mayfly which has legs of two colors as described above, so identification is simple.

When the Nymph is ready to emerge from the stream, it migrates to the shore where it crawls out on a stone and actually emerges from the nymphal shuck after leaving the water. The manner of emergence does not give the fish much of an opportunity to feed on the Subimagos or Duns, but it does give them an excellent opportunity to feed on the Nymph as it clambers out of the water.

A large Leadwing Coachman fished wet along the edge of the stream has proven to be successful when this fly was emerging, and incidentally, the time of emergence is usually just at dusk, so that a wet-fly may be used to an advantage. The ruddy peacock body and the dark wings of the Leadwing Coachman make an excellent representation of *Isonychia* and the writer has no further suggestions to offer, unless it is the substitution of a light ginger or cream hackle for the red hackle with which the Leadwing Coachman is usually tied. Peacock herl appears to be green when dry, but this coloring is prismatic and disappears when the herl is wet, the color then being a ruddy bronze.

On the Schoharie on June 15th, 1935, this fly was in the air literally by the thousands, and although the main hatch occurred on this date, a sufficient number of flies continued to emerge during the remainder of the month to keep the fish excited at dusk. On the Esopus, excellent fishing was experienced while *Isonychia* was emerging and many fishermen reported limit catches on wet-flies suggestive of this natural.

ISONYCHIA BICOLOR WALKER

EMERGENCE DATES

Isonychia bicolor Walker

Stream	City and State	Date
Esopus	Mount Tremper, New York	June 30, 1933
Esopus	Mount Tremper, New York	June 6, 1934
Esopus	Mount Tremper, New York	June 23, 1934
Brodhead	Analomink, Pennsylvania	June 8, 1935
Schoharie	Lexington, New York	June 15, 1935
Esopus	Mount Tremper, New York	June 15, 1935
Esopus	Mount Tremper, New York	June 29, 1935

MAYFLIES AND SEDGES

1. *Ephemera guttulata* Dun (Green Drake)

2. *Ephemera guttulata* Spinner (Coffin Fly)

3. *Psilotreta frontalis* (Dark Blue Sedge)

4. *Isonychia bicolor* Dun
(Leadwing Coachman, see text)

5. *Stenophylax scabripennis*
(Dark Brown Sedge)

CHAPTER VIII

Ephemera guttulata Pictet

Green Drake

Ephemera guttulata Pictet is the scientific name for the large Mayfly which occurs on the trout streams of the East during the early part of June. This fly is known to the fly-fisher as the Green Drake and, after assuming the Spinner stage, as the Coffin Fly.

The Nymph of the Green Drake is of the burrowing type, living in the sand and silt of the stream bottom. Due to its burrowing habits it is doubtful if it furnishes much food for trout, except when it is actually emerging.

After emerging from the stream, the Green Drake usually flies away to a convenient tree, where it undergoes the molt of an entire skin, a practice common to all of the Mayfly family. After the molt, the fly enters the Spinner stage or what is known scientifically as the Imago stage. The general appearance of the Green Drake has changed considerably; in fact, the casual observer would not know that the Green Drake and the Coffin Fly belonged to the same family, much less suspect that it was the same fly.

The Green Drake emerges in great numbers on such streams as it frequents, but unfortunately for the fly-fisher the hatch usually covers a limited space of time, a day or two and at most a week. For this reason the artificial flies representative of the Green Drake are not used to a great extent except when the natural fly is on the water.

In the Catskill Mountain region this fly puts in its appearance during the first week in June, an enormous hatch having been noted by the writer on the lower Beaverkill at Roscoe, N. Y., as early as June 6, 1932. In subsequent years the date of emergence has been approximately the same, until this year, 1935, when the main hatch did not occur on the Beaverkill until June 15th, according to reports from my friend Roy Steenrod.

The Green Drake occurs in New Jersey, especially on the South Branch of the Raritan, and it is abundant in Pennsylvania where it occurs on such streams as the Brodhead and the Lehigh. Green Drakes were collected from the Brodhead as early as June 6th this year. In the Adirondacks, in years when they have an early spring, this fly has been known to appear on the West Branch of the Ausable at Wilmington, N. Y., as early as June 7th; but on the average they do not appear until the second week in June on that stream.

This year the writer arranged his trip so that he would be on the Ausable during the time of the Green Drake hatch, but owing to the prevalence of cloudy and rainy weather they had not put in their appearance up to June 14th, when, due to the pressure of business, it was necessary to return to the city.

It is interesting to note that the Green Drake and its Spinner, the Coffin Fly, seem to prefer fairly warm streams, and that when they start to hatch or emerge on any particular stream they will always appear first on the lower portions of the stream where the water is warmest, gradually moving up stream as the water warms up to the proper temperature for them to emerge. This characteristic is not confined to the Green Drake alone but is equally true of all the *Ephemeridae*, especially those which emerge early in the spring when the water is very cold. Due to the size of the Green Drake, however, it is easy to identify and observe its movements without running the risk of confusion with other species, which danger is always present when trying to observe the habits of the smaller species.

Apparently these flies do not occur on the upper reaches of the Neversink River, but the writer has reports of large hatches on the lower river below Bridgeville, N. Y. They do not seem to appear on the Esopus except in scant numbers, although they are abundant in the next valley, the Schoharie.

The Green Drake is the largest member of the Mayfly family to be encountered on the trout streams of the East, and, while there are larger Mayflies, these larger species are confined to the slow-moving streams and lakes, the St. Lawrence River being especially productive of large *Hexagenia* Mayflies, locally known as Eel Flies.

The size of the Green Drakes varies considerably according to the food available, but the following measurements are fairly average:

Female

Green Drake	*Coffin Fly*
Body—3/4 inch	Body—3/4 inch
Wing—3/4 inch	Wing—3/4 inch
Tails—1 inch	Tails—1 1/8 inches

The males are slightly smaller than the females and may be recognized by the characteristic forceps on the hind end of their abdomens; the long tails, 1 7/8 inches, are also especially noticeable.

While the Spinner of the *Ephemeridae* does not seem to be much relished by trout in our waters, the Coffin Fly is so large and so abundant on the streams where it does occur that some notice must be taken of it. A description of the two flies, i.e., the Green Drake and the Coffin Fly, is given below:

Green Drake

Body—Naples yellow below, with brownish mottlings along the sides
Wings—Transparent, with dark brown or blackish markings
Legs—Lemon yellow
Tails—Three in number, grey with black joints

Coffin Fly

Body—A clear waxy white
Wings—Glossy, with heavy dark brown or blackish markings
Legs—Putty white
Tails—Three in number, clear with black joints

From the description above the origin of the local name Coffin Fly is apparent, as the Spinner of the Green Drake in its sober black and white garb presents a funereal appearance. The Green Drake itself has a pale greenish cast, which is more apparent in the live specimen than in those specimens which have been preserved in alcohol.

This fly does not occur in Great Britain or Europe, and the fly which has been described by Ronalds as the Green Drake, and its Spinner the Grey Drake, belong to a different species, probably either *Ephemera vulgata* or *Ephemera dancia*, both of which are fairly common in the British Isles. The ordinary patterns of Mayflies, known to the fly-fisher as Yellow Mays, are patterned after the British natural flies and not after the fly which occurs in America. This may account for the general lack of success with these patterns on our waters.

The larger the natural fly the more difficult it becomes to make an artificial fly to represent it, which probably accounts for the great number of different patterns of artificials which have been designed to suggest this fly and its British relative.

Very often the largest fish in the stream will surface-feed while the Green Drake is on the water in the daytime, and that is the reason why the Green Drake holds such an important place in the fly-fisher's list of flies, as these monsters, which every fly-fisher dreams of sometime catching, usually confine their activities to minnow chasing or feeding at night. These big fish often rest in the large flat pools, moving up to the faster water only when there is sufficient food coming down to justify their battling the current, with the resulting expenditure of energy. It is, therefore, often necessary to fish for them while they are cruising around in the flat water, especially at the tails of pools where they will pick up scattering flies with the minimum expenditure of energy. When a fish is feeding on Green Drakes in this manner the writer prefers a fly of the Variant type, such as the Gold Variant or the Grey Fox Spider, as these flies land very lightly on the water and are not so likely to scare a fish feeding in thin water as a heavier dressed fly of the exact imitation type. Several good fish were taken by friends of the writer on Variant flies while the Green Drake was on the water this season, including one 17½ inch Brown Trout and one 18¼ inch Brown Trout, both in fine condition, both good fish to be taken on a fly in any water, and especially good for dry-fly in "open water."

There are occasions when the character of the water or the direction of the light necessitates the use of a dry-fly more nearly representative of the natural fly than the Variant type, and the following dressing for the Green Drake has proven to be successful on the Pennsylvania streams. This dressing was developed by Mr. Eugene Connett by a series of experiments lasting over several years:

Body—Natural raffia
Wings—Grizzled cock hackle barbs, dyed the color of the natural wings, tied as divided wings

Legs—Grizzled cock hackle, dyed same as wings
Tail—Three strands cock pheasant's tail
Hook—Hardy Emery No. 7

The above fly entails the use of dyed hackles, and if they cannot be obtained from a tackle dealer, the writer would suggest using a prepared dye, such as Halford's "Green Drake" which may be obtained from any dealer in fly-tying materials.

For the Spinner of the Green Drake, or the fly which is commonly called the Coffin Fly, the following dressing is suggested:

Body—Raffia, bleached as white as possible
Wings—Flank feather from a widgeon or teal tied as a divided wing
Legs—Dark badger cock hackle, or dark honey dun
Tails—Three strands of cock pheasant's tail, long
Hook—Hardy Emery No. 6

The Spinners of the Mayflies being lighter in weight than the Duns or Subimagos, the Coffin Fly may be dressed sparser than the Green Drake.

There are occasions when it is desirable to have some wet-fly suggestive of the Green Drake, and the writer knows of no general pattern better suited than a large Light Cahill tied on a No. 8 Hardy or a No. 6 Bartlett B 7362 hook. A wet-fly will sometimes take a surface feeding fish, which cannot be reached with a dry-fly because of that enemy of all fly-fishers known as "drag." Fish seem to know that a natural fly sitting on the surface of the water has no means of locomotion other than its wings which take it up into the air, and as soon as they see a dry-fly being skittered across the surface they immediately become suspicious and will stop feeding. On the other hand, a Nymph under the surface has means of locomotion, i.e., it can swim, so that any dragging movement imparted to the wet-fly does not cause the feeding fish to become so critical. It does not follow that the fish will take the wet-fly, but the writer is inclined to believe that the chances of taking a good fish on a dragging wet-fly are greater than taking the same fish on a dragging dry-fly.

EMERGENCE DATES

Ephemera guttulata

STREAM	CITY AND STATE	DATE
Beaverkill	Roscoe, New York	June 6, 1934
West Branch Ausable	Wilmington, New York	June 9, 1934
Brodhead	Analomink, Pennsylvania	June 6, 1935
Great Chazy	Ellenburg, New York	June 8, 1935
Schoharie	Lexington, New York	June 15, 1935

Note: The main hatch occurred on the Chazy on June 11th, 1935, and the main hatch occurred on the Schoharie on June 8th, 1935.

CHAPTER IX

Species of Questionable Value

Acentrella

Iron Blue Dun

Acentrella is the generic name for the very small dark blue species of Mayfly which emerges on cold days during the early part of the trout-fishing season. This fly is closely related to the British fly known as the Iron Blue Dun, an excellent fly on the English streams early in the season. However, on the American streams, larger flies emerge at about the same time and the fish seem to take the larger flies in preference to the tiny *Acentrella.*

Specimens have been collected as early as April 21st on the East Branch of the Croton River at Brewster, N. Y., and it is fairly common through New Jersey during the latter part of April. Low water temperatures do not seem to affect this hardy little fly, as the writer has seen it emerge when the water temperature was as low as forty-five degrees.

An artificial tied to represent this fly is of questionable value as the water is usually off-color early in the season and a small fly would hardly be visible to the fish. A blue hackle fly, however, known as a Blue Upright, tied on a No. 14 Hardy hook, is sufficiently near to be useful in case fish are definitely feeding on this fly to the exclusion of larger flies.

POTAMANTHUS DISTINCTIS TRAVER

CREAM VARIANT

Potamanthus distinctis Traver is the scientific name of a large pale yellow Mayfly which emerges from the slow-moving streams and pools of the Catskill regions during the latter part of June. The name *Potamanthus* is of Greek origin and means "riverflower" and from the appearance of the fly it has been properly named.

Louis Rhead, in AMERICAN TROUT STREAM INSECTS, describes a fly which he found on the Beaverkill, which he lists under the month of July as the Golden Drake, and the writer believes that this must be *Potamanthus*.

Eaton notes that flies of the genus *Potamanthus* emerge during the afternoon and that the Nymphs harbor under stones in gently flowing currents at the edge of rapids, and this checks with the writer's observations.

On June 28th, 1933, the writer was fishing on the East Branch of the Delaware below Margaretville, N. Y., where he had the opportunity of seeing this fly emerge in fairly good numbers. However, the high water temperature (78 degrees) must have deterred the fish from feeding on this fly, as not a single rise was noted. Specimens were also collected from the Schoharie at Lexington, N. Y., on July 2nd, 1935.

A large Cream Spider or Variant will serve as a good imitation of this fly.

Blasturus cupidus Say

Blasturus is the scientific name for the large dark May-fly which emerges in the coastal region around New York during the latter part of April.

This fly is confined to the slow-moving streams and reservoirs, or at least it seems to appear on such streams or on the still-water stretches of the faster streams.

Scattered specimens have been collected in the Catskill Mountain region during the month of May, and in the Adirondacks as late as June 23rd, but in the main, the hatch of *Blasturus* which is of interest to the fly-fisher occurs during the latter part of April.

The writer has seen these flies as early as "Opening Day," April 15th, in New Jersey, and much of the early dry-fly fishing is due to the activity of the trout taking this fly.

The size of *Blasturus* varies considerably, those specimens from the mountain regions being much smaller; but despite the difference in size, the one name covers both. The measurements of a female Subimago or Dun from the coastal region is as follows:

Wing—½ inch
Body—½ inch
Tails—outer ⅝ inch, center ⅜ inch

Trout do not seem to be especially selective when feeding on *Blasturus*, especially if they have been shortly released from the hatchery pools. There have been occasions when these hatchery trout would take anything that you threw at them; at other times they can be as choosey as any wild trout. For conditions where the fish are selective, the writer would suggest trying a March Brown, as described under *Stenonema vicarium*, as this fly is of about the same size and coloring as *Blasturus* and while the naturals belong to two different families, the artificial March Brown will serve as a representation of both flies.

Blasturus has no counterpart in the British Isles and, so far as the writer is able to ascertain, is strictly American. It was first described by Thomas Say, the great American entomologist, whose name it bears.

The Duns as they emerge from the stream are a dull brownish-grey in color, the body being decidedly ruddy and banded with brown at the segments. A certain means of identification are the tails which are three in number, but the middle tail is only one-half as long as the outer two.

Dr. Jay R. Traver has made a special study of this fly and some of her observations are as follows:

"Blasturus Nymphs seem to depend for protection more upon coloration than upon swiftness of movement. Quiet backwaters are more favorable for their development. Nymphs will often feign death when disturbed, especially when removed from the water."

Dr. Herman T. Spieth is of the opinion that *Blasturus* deposits its eggs in the open water, but after the Nymphs have about reached maturity they migrate to the still pools where they emerge from the stream. The writer's own observations agree with those of Dr. Spieth.

EMERGENCE DATES

Blasturus cupidus Say

Stream	City and State	Date
Schoharie	Lexington, New York	May 19, 1934
West Branch Ausable	Wilmington, New York	June 23, 1934
Beaverkill	Cook's Falls, New York	May 19, 1935
West Branch Ausable	Wilmington, New York	June 3, 1935
Ausable	Wilmington, New York	June 4, 1935
Ausable	Wilmington, New York	June 12, 1935

Note: Specimens were collected from the East Branch of the Croton River at Brewster, N. Y., on April 21, 1935, but they had apparently emerged from the reservoirs adjacent and not the stream.

Heptagenia

Little Yellow May

There are a number of small yellow flies which emerge just at dark, or in many instances after dark, which belong to the group of Mayflies known as *Heptagenia.*

There is one fly of this family appearing in Great Britain, *Heptagenia sulphurea* or the Little Yellow May Dun, as it is known to the fly-fisher. This English fly does not seem to be attractive to the trout, as Halford reports that he did not find a single specimen in any of the numerous autopsies which he held on chalk stream trout.

These flies have slight markings along the front margin of their fore-wings, and as a rule have jet-black eyes and are small in size, the measurements of a typical fly being as follows:

Heptagenia minerva McDunnough
Female Subimago or Dun

Wing—3/8 inch
Body—1/4 inch
Tails—1/4 inch

Specimens have been collected as follows:

STREAM	CITY AND STATE	DATE
	Heptagenia minerva McDunnough	
Neversink	Bradley, New York	June 10, 1934
	Heptagenia hebe McDunnough	
Neversink	Bradley, New York	June 10, 1934
	Heptagenia juno McDunnough	
Paulinskill	Blairstown, New Jersey	June 2, 1934
	Heptagenia sp.	
West Branch Ausable	Wilmington, New York	June 23, 1934

SPECIES OF QUESTIONABLE VALUE

Leptophlebia

There are two small dark Mayflies belonging to the group known as the *Leptophlebia*. The first, which occurs early in the trout-fishing season, is known as *Leptophlebia adoptiva McDunnough;* the other, which occurs during the second half of June in the Catskill regions, is known as *Leptophlebia mollis Hagen*.

Both of these flies have dark blue wings and three tails, but the markings which characterize the tails of the other three-tailed fly, the *Ephemerella*, are absent. Both flies are small, measuring as follows:

Leptophlebia adoptiva:
Female Subimago or Dun

Wing—5/16 inch
Body—5/16 inch
Tails—1/4 inch

Leptophlebia mollis:
Female Subimago or Dun

Wing—1/4 inch
Body—1/4 inch
Tails—3/16 inch

The male Spinner of the *Leptophlebia mollis* has a clear white body with the rear two segments a brownish red, giving it the same appearance as the male of the British Iron Blue Dun, which belongs to an entirely different family, the genus *Baetis*.

Leptophlebia adoptiva occurs during April and is especially plentiful on the Brodhead during that month; however, it does not seem to attract the trout. Some fly-fishers who fish the Brodhead refer to this fly as the Blue Dun. Incidentally, Halford, that great apostle of the dry-fly, could not find a natural fly to correspond to the artificial fly known as the Blue Dun, but no matter what the fly is called, it still does not seem to have the necessary attraction to cause any excitement among the trout.

In Great Britain there are two flies of the genus *Leptophlebia* and neither one of them has proven useful as a fly to imitate with an artificial. The Claret Dun and the Turkey Brown are both patterned after *Leptophlebia* flies but neither Halford nor Mosely found them attractive to the chalk stream trout.

Specimens have been collected as follows:

Leptophlebia adoptiva McDunnough

STREAM	CITY AND STATE	DATE
Paulinskill	Blairstown, New Jersey	April 22, 1934
Brodhead	Analomink, Pennsylvania	April 20, 1935
Brodhead	Analomink, Pennsylvania	April 24, 1935
Brodhead	Analomink, Pennsylvania	April 27, 1935
Brodhead	Analomink, Pennsylvania	April 28, 1935
Beaverkill	Beaverkill, New York	May 11, 1935
Beaverkill	Beaverkill, New York	May 12, 1935
Beaverkill	Beaverkill, New York	May 13, 1935

SPECIES OF QUESTIONABLE VALUE

Leptophlebia mollis Hagen

STREAM	CITY AND STATE	DATE
Esopus	Mount Tremper, New York	June 30, 1933
Esopus	Mount Tremper, New York	June 9, 1934

The following Mayflies occur in such small numbers on the streams with which the writer is familiar that they have not been considered as suitable for imitation:

Siphlonurus barbarus McDunnough
Siphloplecton basalis Walker
Tricorythus sp.
Baetis sp.
Ameletus ludens Needham

CHAPTER X

The Trichoptera

Caddis

The *Trichoptera* are known to the fly-fisher as the Sedges or Caddis flies for the reason that the larvae or Caddis worms from which these flies hatch have the peculiar faculty of building for themselves a case or house in which they live. There are many species of the *Trichoptera* in America, but as many of them are so nearly alike and have the same habits only two species which are of interest to the fly-fisher will be considered here.

The Caddis flies are not nearly as important to the fly-fisher as the Mayflies for the reason that the Caddis flies, in a great majority of instances, emerge from the stream during the night. The Caddis worms, however, undoubtedly furnish a large proportion of the under-water food and for that reason are of more interest to the fish-culturist than to the fly-fisher. Their life history is as follows:

The newly hatched Caddis worm or creeper immediately starts the construction of a suitable case or house, employing such materials as best suit its needs. The type of case is typical of a specific group of these flies, and every member of that group will build a case of approximately the same material and will pattern it after the same general pattern, so that Caddis worms of the same species may be identified by the type of case in which they live. Some species employ gravel, or vegetable matter, still others a combination of the two materials, binding and cementing them together with a silken substance which the worm itself excretes. The interior of the case is also lined with the same material.

The cases are usually cylindrical, although some species, such as the Grannom, build a tapering case that is perfectly square at the larger end. The cases are open at both ends but the hind end is smaller than the front end.

The newly hatched worms occupy these houses and as they grow and expand they have to enlarge the case by adding more material at the larger end. Some species of Caddis worms fasten their cases to stones and brush submerged in the water, while other species drag their cases around with them as they crawl over the bottom of the stream.

The Caddis case or house is designed for protection from enemies and a very good job it does, as it blends with other material of the stream-bed. If the Caddis worms did not have the benefit of this protective covering they would soon be completely eliminated from this scheme of things, as fish seem to relish them. There are also carnivorous insects, such as the Dragon fly Nymphs and Stone fly Nymphs, which are always ready and waiting to take advantage of any carelessness on the part of a Caddis worm.

The Caddis case, except from the point of view of camouflage, does not furnish much protection against large fish as they do not hesitate to swallow worm, case and all. Stomach examinations of large trout taken this season,

1935, disclosed Caddis cases two inches in length. The worm is apparently dissolved out of the case by the action of the juices in the trout's stomach and the case itself taken care of in the regular elimination.

When the Caddis worm reaches maturity, or reaches the point where it is ready to enter into its pupal stage, it seals up the front entrance to its case with a grating, the pattern of which is often the means of identifying the worm inside, each species having a particular pattern of grating. The object of this grating is to afford protection to the worm while it is in the pupal state, during which time wings are acquired. The grating permits water to flow through the case, thus providing the necessary oxygen to preserve life.

When the pupa, having acquired wings, awakes from this period of dormancy, it tears open the grating and emerges. The pupa is still swathed in a thin membrane but the middle pair of legs is left free of this sheath and, using this middle pair of legs, the pupa swims to the surface where the sheath is broken and the winged fly takes flight.

After arriving at the winged state the Caddis fly does not undergo any further change in structure, as does the May-fly, but is ready for mating and egg-laying operations at once. The Caddis flies do not eat after reaching the winged state because their mouth parts are left enmeshed in the grating when they tear it open to emerge from the case.

The Caddis flies have two pairs of wings, the hind pair usually being shorter and generally broader than the front pair; when at rest the hind wings are completely covered by the fore pair which are folded alongside the body, meeting over the top of the body in the shape of an inverted V. The wings are covered with short hairs, particularly noticeable along the margins, and while these hairs may not always be visible to the naked eye they can easily be seen with the aid of a low power magnifying glass.

During flight the two pairs of wings are often joined together so that the fly appears to have only a single pair of wings. During flight the body is held in a horizontal position except in some cases where the female fly, when carrying eggs, flies with her body weighted down and pitched towards the rear. This is a means of distinguishing Caddis flies from Stone flies, as the latter in flight carry their bodies in a vertical position. All Caddis flies have a pair of fairly long antennae, which are held out in front, even while the insect is in flight. They have no tails.

About the only fly with which the Caddis flies can be easily confused is the American Alder (*Sialis infumata*), and, while there is a marked resemblance, the Alder may be identified by the absence of hairs on the wings.

During the early part of the trout-fishing season a great many Caddis flies are in evidence but it is seldom that they are actually seen to emerge from the water. It is, therefore, apparent that the flies have emerged during the night. Many of these early Caddis flies belong to the family known as *Brachycentrus*, in which family is included the fly which occurs in Great Britain, *Brachycentrus subnubilus*, known to all fly-fishers as the dingy little Sedge which carries its eggs in a green mass at its posterior: the Grannom.

The American counterpart of the British Grannom is what the late Louis Rhead termed the Shad Fly. This fly occurs throughout the Catskill region and is also common in New Jersey and Pennsylvania. In New Jersey it is in evidence on the warmer streams as early as April 20th. It then ranges up through the Catskill regions where enormous flights of this insect are visible during the middle of May. This year, 1935, literally millions of Shad Flies were seen moving up the Beaverkill River at Cooks Falls, N. Y., in great clouds. Mr. Martin E. Mosely, of the British Museum, is of the opinion that the value of this fly lies chiefly in providing an immense quantity of food for trout at the season when they most require it, i.e., quite early in spring. The same condition undoubtedly holds true in America and the writer is of the opinion that the great bulk of these flies consumed by the fish are taken under water, possibly during the night, as he cannot recall ever seeing a trout definitely rising for the winged fly.

Halford shows a dry-fly pattern of the Grannom in his first book FLOATING FLIES, but in his later writings he intimates that the dry-fly was not very successful; he then tried an imitation of the Grannom pupa which had to be fished as a semi-submerged fly or a wet-fly. He later abandoned this fly as being at variance with true dry-fly practice.

Dr. Baigent, that celebrated Yorkshire fly-fisher, who is the originator of the dry-fly known as the Baigent's Brown, states that it will often take trout while the Grannom is on the water in England. While the writer has been quite successful with other patterns of Baigent's flies he has not been successful in taking trout when the Grannom is on the water in this country. This, perhaps, is not due to any shortcoming on the part of the fly but is simply due to the fact that the trout have been gorged on the pupa and will not bother to take a surface fly.

Mr. Mosely states that the female Grannom, when laying her eggs, probably descends into the water to deposit them by climbing down some posts or weed stems and possibly never rises again to the surface. He states that he "has found individuals attached to the weed several inches below the surface of the water and quite dead." The time of emergence, at night, and this manner of depositing its eggs, do not make this fly a suitable one for imitation.

Dark Blue Sedge

During the second week in June in the Adirondacks, in company with the large Mayfly known as the Green Drake, comes a Caddis fly which is sometimes taken by the trout in preference to the Green Drake. This fly is of a brownish-blue coloring and specimens in the writer's collection measure body 3/8 inch, wings 5/8 inch. Specimens of this fly were collected on June 8th, 1934, by Byron Blanchard, who states that they were in evidence during the day and that the fish were definitely feeding on them. This fly has been identified by Dr. Cornelius Betten of Cornell University as *Psilotreta frontalis*.

In Great Britain there is a fly which is known scientifically as *Sericostoma personatum*, which occupies a similar position and emerges in company with the English Green Drake. This fly is known to the British fly-fisher as the Welshman's Button. The American fly as yet has not been named by the fly-fisher, but from its coloring it might easily be called the Dark Blue Sedge. As the Dark Blue Sedge is on the water during the day a dry-fly tied to imitate it as follows may be used with hope of success.

Body—Brown seal's fur
Hackle—Dark rusty blue dun cock tied Palmer. A few turns of white hackle aid visibility
Rib—Gold wire binding hackle
Hook—No. 11 Hardy

Brown Sedge

During July and August large brown Caddis flies are fairly plentiful after dark and they are easily attracted by lights. A number of specimens were collected by this method on the Neversink River during August of 1934. These large brown flies belong to two different genera, namely, *Platyphylax* and *Stenophylax*. They are so nearly alike in size and coloring that the fly-fisher need not bother to try to differentiate between them. They are large flies, the body measuring ½ inch and the wing ¾ inch.

It is of interest to note, however, that the *Stenophylax* has quite a musty odor which probably gives rise to the name of Fetid Brown, a name occurring in some of the older books on fly-fishing.

A great many artificial flies used for night fishing are doubtlessly designed to suggest these large brown Caddis flies. The following dressing is representative of *Stenophylax scabripennis* (the Brown Sedge):

Body—Amber seal mixed with light tan fur from a hare's poll
Hackle—Light red cock tied in Palmer fashion
Rib—Gold tinsel
Wings—Wing quill feather of a bittern
Hook—No. 8 Hardy or No. 6 Bartlett B 7362

While the Brown Sedge is primarily a night fly with strictly nocturnal habits, a dry-fly suggestive of the Brown Sedge may often be fished during the daytime with success. The Brown Bi-visible, which is merely a brown hackle with a few wisps of white tackle tied in front to give visibility, the invention of Mr. E. R. Hewitt, is a very good dry-fly to use as representative of the Brown Sedge. The dressing of the Brown Bi-visible is familiar to all anglers.

The expression "hackle tied Palmer fashion" was originally used to describe flies in imitation of the large caterpillars which, because of their wanderings, were often called Palmers in comparing them with the Crusaders who carried palms on their expeditions. However, in the case of the Sedge flies, the Palmer-tied hackle is probably viewed by the trout as being suggestive of wings fluttering alongside the body.

STONE FLIES AND CADDIS CASES

1. *Taeniopteryx fasciata* (Early Brown Stone Fly)

2. *Perla capitata* female in flight

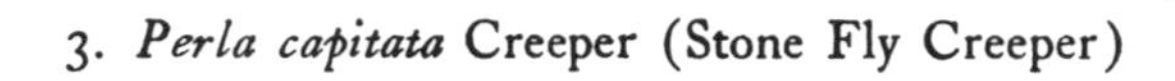

3. *Perla capitata* Creeper (Stone Fly Creeper)

4. *Brachycentrus* (See text)

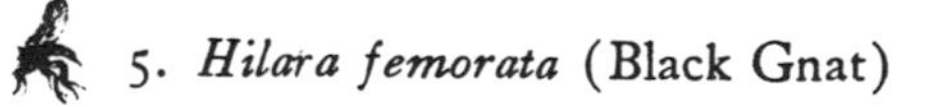

5. *Hilara femorata* (Black Gnat)

6. *Lasius interjectus* (Brown Ant)

7. *Psilotreta frontalis* (Caddis case and worm)

8. *Stenophylax scabripennis* (Caddis case and worm)

9. *Brachycentrus* (Caddis case and worm)

CHAPTER XI

PLECOPTERA

STONE FLIES

IN general the *Plecoptera* or Stone flies are of little use to the fly-fisher; but there are times early in the trout-fishing season, or in July and August, when the May-flies are not in evidence, and then the Stone flies may assist in the killing of a trout.

Up to a few years ago little study had been made of this particular family of flies, only one book having been written about them, namely, HISTOIRE NATURELLE DES INSECTES NEUROPTERES, PREMIERE MONOGRAPHIE, FAMILLE DES PERLIDES. This book, as the title indicates, is written in French, and the author is no other than that pioneer in entomology, Pictet. This book was published in 1841–42.

A second book on the Stone flies has recently been written by Drs. J. G. Needham and P. W. Claassen, and published by the Thomas Say Foundation, under the name PLECOPTERA OF NORTH AMERICA. This book is a scientific treatise describing some twenty-four families and some two hundred odd species of Stone flies which occur in America. Many of the species are so nearly alike that the differences can be seen only with the aid of a powerful microscope, and while it is no doubt necessary to draw fine lines of distinction in a scientific work, the fly-fisher may well limit his artificial flies to general patterns which present a suggestion of many species.

Stone flies are often confused with the Caddis flies or Sedges, but there are some general characteristics which will enable the fly-fisher to distinguish between these groups without difficulty.

When at rest, the Stone flies fold their wings flat over their backs in a horizontal position. The Caddis flies or Sedges when at rest fold their wings along their sides, with the upper edges meeting over the top of the back in the form of an inverted V. In flight the Stone flies carry their bodies in a vertical position and all four wings are clearly visible as separate units, while the Caddis flies fly with the body in a horizontal position, and the wings are often interlocked so that they appear to have only two wings, while in fact they actually have four wings.

PLECOPTERA OF NORTH AMERICA has some valuable information of general interest and a few excerpts are quoted as follows:

"Stone flies in their immature stage are all inhabitants of running water and are to be sought as adults in the vicinity of streams. The immature stage [Creeper] resembles in general the adult, but the wings are lacking, and they always occur in the water, either under stones or under drifted leaves, débris, etc. The mouth parts are of the biting type and are well developed. As far as we know, all the creepers possess long, filamentous, many-segmented tails.

. . . Gills may occur in tufts or as a single filament and are placed on either side of the thorax, on the sides and tip of the abdomen or in the cervical region."

Most of the Stone fly creepers which have come to the attention of the writer have their gills on the thorax, and as a general rule this is one of the best means of distinguishing them from the Nymphs of the Mayfly, which carry their gills along the sides of their abdomen.

Quoting further from PLECOPTERA OF NORTH AMERICA:

"At least one year seems to be required to complete the life cycle, and in some of the larger species two or even three years may be consumed. . . . Heretofore, Stone flies have usually been considered as carnivorous, but the stomach contents of a number of creepers indicate that some species feed on vegetable matter only, while others prey upon animal forms as well as feeding on vegetable matter. . . . Most Stone flies do not feed in the adult stage, but some have well developed mouth parts."

Some early writers on angling flies were under the impression that Stone flies always dropped their eggs while flying over the water, but it has been the writer's observation that the female Stone flies actually drop down to the surface of the stream when depositing their eggs. The eggs are not held together in a mass by a gelatinous sac, as are the eggs of the Mayflies, but each egg is a free unit. Specimens carrying eggs, when collected, immediately void the eggs when placed in the collecting fluid.

Stone flies do not undergo a pupal stage, as do the Caddis flies; neither do they undergo a molt after arriving at the winged stage, as do the Mayflies. The change from the creeper stage to the winged stage, apart from the acquiring of wings, is slight. It has been thought that Stone fly creepers crawl out of the stream on some convenient rock or tree, where the actual shedding of the nymphal shuck took place, and the average fly-fisher is no doubt familiar with these shucks which are often seen on exposed rocks along the banks of rapid streams; in fact, the writer has seen these shucks in trees fifteen feet off the ground. However, there are conditions where the change from the creeper stage to the winged stage may take place in the water as illustrated by the following incident:

During the early Spring of 1934 the writer had occasion to visit the trout hatchery at Hackettstown, N. J., and incidentally also to look over the condition of some of the New Jersey trout streams. The Musconetcong River flows through Hackettstown and as it is usually heavily stocked with trout, it was thought advisable to visit the stream above Hackettstown and see if there were any indications of feeding trout. Fish were feeding actively in a large pool which had been formed by the construction of a small concrete dam, but it was some time before we could find out just what was causing this surface feeding so early in the year. The date was April 8, 1934. Finally we discovered a few small brownish-blue flies struggling on the surface of the water near the dam; these we secured and found them to be Stone flies. They were identified by Dr. Needham as *Taeniopteryx fasciata*, but for simplicity let us call them an Early Brown Stone fly or just an Early Brown. There are a number of different species of the same general size and coloring occurring both in Great Britain and America; in fact, Ronalds notes an early Stone fly which he calls the February Red. The American Stone fly, however, occurring early in the trout-fishing season, is both larger and darker than the fly which Ronalds describes. Of course, the condition described above is somewhat artificial, as the creepers which occupied the stream before the dam had been constructed had to emerge the best way they could and they probably thought that straight up was the shortest route; but it was not a very safe route as practically every creeper that reached the surface was taken by a trout before it could get off the water.

Nymphal shucks of the large Stone fly Creeper have also been noted floating downstream in the Beaverkill at Roscoe, N. Y., but it is probable that the shucks were left just at the water's edge and a slight rise in the water-level loosened them.

In general the habits of the Stone flies are not such that artificial dry-flies suggestive of them can be fished with much hope of success and the writer has limited his artificials to two, both tied as wet-flies. The first, the Early Brown Stone fly, is dressed as follows:

Wings—Two hackle points from a dark rusty dun cock, tied flat over the body

Body—Dark brown hare's fur mixed with claret (dyed) seal
Legs—Dark rusty cock's hackle, soft
Tail—Two barbs from pheasant's tail, short
Hook—No. 10 Hardy or No. 8 Bartlett B 7362
Silk—Orange

William Chandler of Neversink, N. Y., a close friend of the late Theodore Gordon, writes that Gordon tied a similar fly, which was very effective for early fishing on the Neversink River.

This Early Brown Stone fly is widely distributed and is abundant on the Esopus during the latter part of April; and it is in evidence during the day, which is unusual for a Stone fly as they generally emerge during the very early hours of the morning, before daylight.

The large Stone fly Creeper is an excellent insect to imitate, especially when it is to be used early in the morning. On one occasion the writer had the courage to get out at 4 A.M. to fish the lower Beaverkill and had the good fortune to kill two fine Brown Trout on a wet-fly suggestive of the Stone fly Creeper. Both of these fish had gorged themselves on the natural creeper, which was evidently in the act of migrating towards the edge of the stream to emerge, and their stomachs were distended to the size of a man's fist. Apparently all of the creepers had been swallowed in a short space of time, as digestion, which is rapid, had not started to affect the first creepers swallowed. This particular creeper has been identified as *Perla capitata*, by Dr.

Needham, and is sufficiently typical to be used as a general pattern.

The dressing for the wet-fly suggestive of the above creeper is as follows:

Wings—Widgeon flank feather, tied flat over back
Body—Amber seal (dyed), mixed with the light sandy fur from a hare's poll
Legs—Grizzled cock's hackle, soft
Tail—Barbs from cock pheasant's tail feather, long
Hook—No. 8 Hardy or No. 6 Bartlett B 7362
Silk—Primrose

While the creeper has no wings, the widgeon feather with its alternate black and white markings is very suggestive of the upper portion of the creeper's body. A rib of gold wire, while not absolutely necessary, may also be added.

There are several varieties of small yellow Stone flies, which are generally in evidence fluttering about the bushes on most rocky streams. These are called Yellow Sallies and are not of a great deal of use to the fly-fisher. However, there are occasions when it seems necessary to fish the smaller rocky streams and a small Ginger Hackle, which is suggestive of the small Yellow Sallies, will usually take fish.

CHAPTER XII

Sialis infumata
The American Alder

The American Alder is a fly which is encountered along the banks of almost any trout stream in the Catskills during the months of May and June. Due to its habits the Alder is seldom seen on the water, and for that reason little attention has been paid to it by the American fly-fisher.

In England the Alder has been copied by the fly-tyer for hundreds of years; in fact, Major Hills, author of A History of Flyfishing for Trout, is of the opinion that the Alder may be one of the original flies referred to in one of the earliest printed books, Fysshe and Fysshynge, by Dame Juliana Berners, published in 1496.

In England the fly known as the Alder is not used to any great extent as a dry-fly, but when tied as a wet-fly its reputation as a killer is second to none. Incidentally, the Alder was one of the favorite flies of Charles Kingsley, author of Chalk Stream Studies.

In America the Alder wet-fly is imported from England and, of course, the artificial fly is patterned after the British Alder, known scientifically as *Sialis lutaria.* Neither the wet-fly nor the dry-fly commercially sold by shops has been particularly successful on American waters, due no doubt to the fact that the American Alder, scientifically *Sialis infumata*, is quite different from the British Alder as far as the shade of coloring is concerned and the imported flies are not good representations of the natural fly as found on our streams.

The writer has collected the American Alder, *Sialis infumata*, in the Catskills as early as May 15th and in the Adirondacks as late as June 20th. While there has been no opportunity of comparing these specimens with the natural British flies, written descriptions by Halford, in DRY FLY ENTOMOLOGY, as well as the colored illustrations given in Mosely's DRY FLY FISHERMAN'S ENTOMOLOGY indicate that the British Alder is of a brownish cast, while the American representative of the Alder is much darker; in fact, it has been described as black.

Before suggesting a dressing for the artificial fly it might be well to consider some of the general characteristics of the fly, so that it may be identified on the stream.

The American Alder belongs to the family of flies known as the *Sialididae* and the species which is of particular interest to the fly-fisher is known as *Sialis infumata*. It is also interesting to note that the *Corydalis*, whose Nymph is known to all bass-fishers as the Helgramite, is also a member of the *Sialididae* group.

The Alder, like most water-bred flies, spends the greater part of its life in a larval state, but due to the fact that the creeper or larva burrows into the stream bed to a depth of five or six inches, it is doubtful if fish have much of an opportunity of becoming acquainted with the Alder in its larval state.

The complete life cycle is as follows: The female deposits the fertile eggs on the underside of bridges or bushes which overhang running water, so that the larva when hatched will drop directly into the running water. Scientific observers of the habits of this fly have noticed that the fly apparently knows the limits of the running water, as eggs are not deposited where the larva would fall on the bank.

The larvae upon hatching drop into the water and settle to the bottom, where they burrow into the stream bed. Their close relative, the Helgramite, makes short work of those who do not take the trouble to dig in.

The larval state lasts for two years, during which time the larva reaches maturity; it then crawls out of the stream on to the bank and, traveling back from the stream for a distance of a few feet, burrows into the ground for a depth of several inches. Here it undergoes a short pupal period, during which time the change from a larva or creeper to a winged fly takes place. From its pupal burrow it digs its way to the surface and flies away as a complete fly, ready to mate and die.

In its winged state the Alder does not take any food as the mouth parts, which served it so well during the larval stage, are now atrophied and useless. The Alder does not shed its skin after becoming a winged fly, as is the case with the Mayflies or *Ephemeridae*.

The Alder resembles some of the Caddis flies, or *Trichoptera,* as they are called, but is not so quick on the wing; neither is it much of a runner. Specimens are easy to collect. Naturals in the writer's collection measure as follows:

Body—7/16 inch
Wing—1/2 inch
Antennae—1/4 inch
Tail—None

The general coloring is of a very dark brown, almost black. The wings are smooth, while the Caddis flies have wings covered with short hairs. The Caddis flies are the only flies with which the Alder could be easily confused.

In England the Alder is sometimes confused with the Caddis fly which appears at the same time as the Green Drake. This Caddis fly is known to the fly-fisher as the Welshman's Button or, scientifically, as *Sericostoma personatum.* In America we have a fly which occupies a similar position in our streams, known scientifically as *Psilotreta frontalis;* but as far as the writer is aware no name has been given to it by the American fly-fisher, although from its coloring it might be called the Dark Blue Sedge.

Aside from the rare occasions when the Alders are blown on to the water by some sudden storm, it is doubtful if the natural fly gets on the water in any large quantity, except when the females are spent from their egg-laying. The spent females undoubtedly fall on to the surface of the stream and apparently sink without much struggling, as their life work is finished and their energy completely used up with the laying of the eggs. This is probably the reason for the fact that the artificial Alder has always been fished successfully as a wet-fly in England and, for the same reason, it is useless as a dry-fly.

The artificial flies sold in the American tackle shops are patterned after the British Alder and are much too light in coloring, and in the writer's experience have not proven themselves to be a successful fly fished either wet or dry.

The Leadwing Coachman wet-fly more nearly approaches the appearance of the American Alder than any pattern of general fly which has come to the writer's notice. However, the Leadwing Coachman can be improved upon, and the following dressing is suggested:

American Alder (*Sialis infumata*)

Wings—Dark feather from the secondary wing quill of a black duck, tied pent-shaped over the body
Body—Bronze peacock herl (all peacock herl turns a bronzy black when wet)
Rib—Rusty red sewing silk, tied reverse to herl, binding herl
Legs—Cochy-bondhu, a cock hackle, not too stiff (Cochy-bondhu is a red hackle with a black center and tips)
Tail—None
Hook—No. 9 Hardy or No. 8 Bartlett B 7362
Silk—Claret
Head—Black varnish

EMERGENCE DATES

Sialis infumata

East Branch Delaware	Arena, New York	May 21, 1934
West Branch Ausable	Wilmington, New York	June 20, 1934
Ausable	Wilmington, New York	June 10, 1935
Ausable	Wilmington, New York	June 11, 1935
Ausable	Wilmington, New York	June 14, 1935

CHAPTER XIII

Ants

Ants are land-bred insects, pure and simple, but there are occasions when they get on the water in sufficiently large quantities to be worthy of notice on the part of the fly-fisher.

The ants get on the water usually during the times of their mating flights which occur during the spring and summer, different species mating at different times. This year, 1935, on June 2nd and 3rd there were a great number of large brown wood ants, known as Carpenter Ants (scientifically, *Camponotus ligniperda Novaboracensis*), very much in evidence in the wooded section of the Ausable River. These insects were getting on to the water in sufficiently large numbers for the trout to be feeding on them. However, due to the fact that Mayflies were also in season and on the water in scattering numbers an artificial fly suggestive of the Mayfly would take fish, although the fish were actually feeding on ants.

It has been the writer's opinion for some time that Brown Trout when feeding on land insects, such as ants and beetles, etc., are not selective to the point of demanding an exact imitation of the particular insect on which they are feeding, but are very likely to take an artificial fly that is suggestive of one of the *Ephemeridae* then in season. This opinion has been recently confirmed by an experience on the Esopus where a large Brown Trout was taken on a dry-fly suggestive of the Mayfly *Stenonema fuscum* and a subsequent stomach examination disclosed the fact that the trout had been feeding on large wood Carpenter Ants.

These ants are large insects measuring about one-half inch in length, and probably got on the water in considerable numbers. However, as they were in evidence on only two days the trout are not sufficiently well acquainted with them to become selective when feeding on them.

During July and August, when a Mayfly or *Ephemerida* is seldom seen, it is quite possible that fish will be selective in their feeding, especially as concerns the small brown lawn ant which has been described as being one of the most common of all insects.

This group of ants mates during the summer and early fall, and as the active members who are to mate acquire wings prior to leaving the family nest, and also due to the fact that actual mating takes place while in flight, considerable numbers of them fall on the streams and are taken by the trout. During the latter part of August, 1934, the writer noticed a heavy flight of these ants at Bradley, New York, and a great many of them fell on the Neversink River creating quite a commotion and feeding activity on the part of the smaller trout.

The larger fish, which we knew were occupying a particular pool, were apparently not willing to risk exposure by surface-feeding in the bright sunlight as they did not start to feed until after dark. However, the smaller fish were grabbing everything in sight. This particular family of ants, which was in flight on this occasion, was *Lasius interjectus Mayr* and has been so identified by Dr. William S. Creighton of the College of the City of New York.

Louis Rhead, in his book AMERICAN TROUT STREAM INSECTS, describes a Sage Green Ant as occurring in the month of August, but the writer doubts if this is a separate species, for, although the females of the *Lasius* group are yellowish in color, they might, when in flight and viewed against the blue sky, appear to be quite green.

Most of the commercial patterns of flies representative of ants are too large to suggest the Brown Ant, *Lasius interjectus Mayr*, and the writer would suggest the following dressing as being more nearly in keeping with the appearance of this insect:

Body—⅓ pheasant's tail, ⅓ rusty red silk, ⅓ pheasant's tail
Hackle—Rusty red to suggest wings as well as legs
Hook—Bartlett B 7362, size No. 12

This fly is fished either wet or semi-submerged as the ants, being land insects, are not capable of running on the surface of the water, nor do they have the faculty for alighting gently when they fall. Hence, they kick around, very much bedraggled and half-submerged.

CHAPTER XIV

Black Gnats

When there are no Mayflies about, trout seem to spend a great deal of their time feeding on tiny black insects which swarm a few inches above the surface of the water. These flies belong to the great order of insects known as the *Diptera*, so called because of the fact they have two wings.

According to Dr. C. H. Curran of the Museum of Natural History in New York City, the flies most commonly found swarming over running water are the genus *Hilara*, and the particular species common in the East is *Hilara femorata*. Due to their complicated aerial motions these flies are also known as the Dance Flies.

The larvae of these flies live in the silt along the margin and bed of the stream and probably furnish a fair percentage of food for the smaller fish. Very little is known of their life history. When trout are feeding on the swarming winged fly they seem oblivious to everything which goes on around them, and appear to concentrate every effort upon getting a meal of these flies. Taking into consideration the minute size of the flies, they have quite a job on their fins, as it were. Apparently, trout will leap out of the water, evidently bent upon knocking down several flies at one time, and then picking them up at their leisure. It has been the writer's observation that this method of feeding is generally practiced on still pools, where the cripples cannot readily escape.

These flies are very small and perhaps may be best represented by a badger cock hackle tied on a No. 15 Hardy hook. No tail or body is necessary for this fly as the dark center of the badger hackle is a sufficient suggestion to represent the body while the clear yellow tips of the hackle suggest the wings in motion.

Very often a large fly of the Variant type will prove successful when fish are feeding on these tiny flies. A recent experience on the Brodhead in Pennsylvania confirms this fact. A big trout was seen feeding against a ledge on the far side of a large pool, and from the frequency and the character of the rise it was evident that the fish was feeding on these tiny insects. A small Badger Hackle was tried but the light was too poor to follow such a small fly on the water and a Light Gold Variant was substituted. This fly was taken the first time it passed over the feeding location of the fish and a subsequent stomach examination confirmed the fact that the fish had been feeding on tiny black gnats, his gullet and stomach being literally crammed with them.

PART III

NYMPHS

1. *Stenonema vicarium* Nymph, clambering type (American March Brown, wet)

2. *Ephemera guttulata* Nymph, burrowing type (Light Cahill, wet)

3. *Acentrella* Nymph, swimming type (See text)

4. *Ephemerella invaria* Nymph, creeping type (Quill Gordon, wet)

CHAPTER I

Nymphs

The aquatic stage of the Mayfly is known as the Nymph and it develops from the egg which the winged fly has deposited in running water. Most species of Mayflies with which the fly-fisher is concerned lay their eggs in the rapid broken water known as riffles. The reason for this is that the incubation of the egg requires oxygen, and oxygen is more abundant in broken water. There are, of course, some species which inhabit lakes and ponds, whose eggs do not require so much oxygen for incubation; but these flies are of little use to the stream fly-fisher.

Pictet classified the Nymphs of the Mayflies in accordance with their method of locomotion and habitat, and the same procedure will be followed here:

Type	Typical Fly	Scientific Name
Burrowers	American Green Drake	*Ephemera guttulata*
Clamberers	American March Brown	*Stenonema vicarium*
Swimmers	American Iron Blue Dun	*Acentrella*
Crawlers	Hendrickson	*Ephemerella invaria*

The burrowing Nymphs spend their lives under water digging tunnels in the soft sand and silt of the stream bed, and apart from the time when they are actually emerging or hatching into winged flies, it is exceedingly doubtful if the trout have a chance to feed on Nymphs of this class. The Nymph of the American Green Drake, and its Spinner the Coffin Fly, is typical of this class of Nymph.

The clambering type Nymph is flattened and appears to be especially designed by nature for clinging to and living under stones. Some species have well-developed discs on the under side of their abdomen, with which they cling to the stones by suction; others depend entirely upon their claws for clinging. During periods of high water and flood, the stones of the stream bed are usually rolled about with great force, resulting in high mortality to the clinging and clambering Nymphs. After the water clears, or is clearing, every trout in the river is busy gathering up the cripples, and tremendous execution can be done with a wet-fly, in case the fly-fisher is fortunate enough to be on the stream at such a time. The Nymph of the American March Brown, *Stenonema vicarium*, is typical of the clambering type Nymph.

The swimming Nymphs occur only in small numbers in our fast streams and, as they are all small in size as compared with the clambering type Nymphs, it hardly seems worth while to consider them from the standpoint of imitating them. This type of Nymph is abundant in the chalk streams of England, and nymph-fishing was developed there in order to catch fish that were visibly feeding on the Nymph and could not be induced to take a dry-fly. The American Iron Blue Dun, *Acentrella*, is typical of this class.

The crawling Nymphs are those Nymphs which are not equipped for digging, clambering or swimming. This class of Nymph has to depend upon the slowness of their movements in the water, to escape their enemies. These Nymphs are usually found near the banks of the stream, where they cover themselves with débris, and by their stealthy movements manage to survive without being eaten. The Nymph of the Hendrickson dry-fly, *Ephemerella invaria*, is typical of this class.

For a short time prior to the change from the nymphal stage to the winged stage, there is considerable activity on the part of the Nymph, and no doubt the Nymph realizes in its own way that an important event in its life is about to take place. In any case, the Nymph has to make the trip from its abode to the surface of the stream where the actual transformation takes place, and if everything goes well, the nymphal shuck is broken, the winged fly emerges and in due course flies away. Trout take advantage of this opportunity to get a meal and many is the Nymph that is intercepted on its journey to the surface. From the point of view of supplying nourishment, the freshly emerged fly, which is called a "Dun," is probably the choicest morsel which appears on the trout's menu. The cast-off nymphal shuck does not contain anything of value as food, and as the winged flies do not eat after they have assumed the winged stage, the high point in food value is just when they emerge. The female flies also are filled with eggs, which is energy in a highly concentrated form. Happily for the fly-fisher the trout seem to prefer the newly hatched Duns to either the Nymph or Spinner, and as the time of their emergence is usually spread over several hours, or in some cases days and weeks, the angler fishing with an imitation of the Dun has many productive hours on the stream.

Were it not for this trip from the bottom of the stream to the surface, it is doubtful if we would ever have dry-fly fishing. Trout have more protection from their enemies when they are deep in the water, but the eagerness with which they feed on the ascending Nymphs causes them to ascend to the upper levels of the water, where they take the newly hatched Duns from the surface. It is when trout are feeding on these Duns that the fly-fisher says that trout are "rising." Of course, trout take other flies as well, but no fly seems to have such a stimulating effect on a trout's appetite as the sudden appearance of a quantity of Nymphs emerging as Duns.

A trout feeding on Nymphs in the lower levels of water, or a fish grubbing around on the bottom of the stream, is a better prospect for the bait-fisher than for the fly-fisher; but it is when the Nymphs start to ascend to the surface to emerge as flies that the trout leaves his grubbing and starts to look for surface food. This feeding in the upper levels is not without its dangers, as a fish near the surface is a ready mark for birds of prey, such as the Blue Heron and the Osprey. These birds take their toll, but it is man, with all the knowledge of the ages at his command, all the tools of modern science at his finger tips, that makes the killing. A slender rod, a silken line, an invisible leader of hairlike fineness, a counterfeit fly cunningly devised of fur and feathers and steel, a surface-feeding trout, the cast, the strike, the net, and another trout goes the way of all flesh.

There has been a great deal written about Nymphs and nymph-fishing during the past few years, but results obtained by a great many expert anglers of the writer's acquaintance have not been as successful as they had hoped. The reason for this is simple; if a trout is feeding on the ascending Nymphs this fish is the very best possible prospect for the dry-fly man, for sooner or later this fish will be taking the freshly hatched Duns from the surface. If a fish can be taken on the dry-fly most anglers of the writer's acquaintance would prefer taking it by that method. If it could be predicted with a reasonable degree of accuracy just when any given species of fly was ready to emerge, an artificial copy of that specific Nymph might be useful; but so far as the writer is aware the first warning of the hatch is the actual appearance of the Duns.

In large waters where it is necessary to canvass a wide area in order to locate fish—especially at times when there is no indication of a surface-feeding fish—the writer would suggest trying a seasonable wet-fly in the fast water or riffles. Fish often prospect for Stone fly Creepers and Nymphs in this thin, fast water, and a wet-fly can be sunk deep enough to attract them. There are a great many patterns of wet-flies, tied for both downstream or upstream methods of fishing. Flies tied for use in fishing downstream usually have hard hackles, so that they will not mat and cover the body of the fly as it is drawn across and against the current. Flies tied for fishing up-stream have soft hackles, so that the hackles will readily respond to the influence of the current as the fly is carried down-stream without any action being imparted to it by the angler. Most wet-flies are doubtless taken by the fish as suggestive of some form of insect life, Creepers, Nymphs, Caddis pupae, or even small minnows or fry, and as this underwater life is so varied and multitudinous, it hardly seems worth while trying to imitate any specific Nymph. There are, however, some general forms that are found in most streams, and the following wet-flies, while they suggest specific forms of insect life, are sufficiently general to cover ordinary requirements:

Early season, rocky streams—Early Brown Stone fly
Early season, large streams—March Brown (American)
Mid-season, large streams—Light Cahill
Mid-season, large streams, early morning—
Stone fly Creeper
Late season, large streams, evenings—Brown Sedge

Quill bodied flies, such as the Quill Gordon and the Mallard Quill, are often successful in clear streams.

For upstream fishing, a trimmed Hare's Ear wet-fly with only the stubs of the wings left on, is about as good a Nymph as has come to the attention of the writer.

CHAPTER II

VARIANTS

VARIANT is the name given to flies of the long hackle type, which are in fact variations of some standard pattern.

The credit for designing this type of fly has been given to that ardent and enthusiastic fly-fisher of Yorkshire, England, Dr. William Baigent, who has been tying lightly hackled spiders or Variants for the past thirty years.

Some years ago it was the writer's good fortune to get an excellent neck of hackle from a Rusty Blue Dun Game Cock, just the thing for tying the long hackled dry-fly called the Blue Variant. This fly was a success from the start, especially for Rainbow Trout on the Esopus in the Catskills. A letter to Dr. Baigent, telling him of the excellent work done by his pattern, brought forth the following reply: "I am very pleased and much interested to know the 'Baigent' flies kill so well in America. I receive letters from New Zealand, Australia, Tasmania, France; in fact, all over the world with nothing but praise as to their killing powers. This is exactly what I anticipated and can quite understand the reason. Thirty years ago or more I commenced with the new idea of making flies according to the wishes of the trout rather than an exact *bench* copy of the natural, by practical tests to find out what would stimulate the trout's 'investigatory reflex,' as Pavlov calls it. After years of trial and noting results I further tried what could be done by optics, that is, altered refraction, etc. . . . and the results of those years of work are found partly but not completely in the two series of flies in Hardy's catalog."

The writer is partial to flies of this type, especially when fishing flat water, or still pools where it is necessary to have a dry-fly which lands on the water with a minimum of fuss. Trout feeding on large naturals will often take a feeding position in the flat water at the tail of a pool and it requires careful approach and still more careful casting to take fish under these conditions.

For Brown Trout the following patterns have been particularly successful, and the writer can recommend them, if the hackle is of good quality:

Blue Variant, Gold Body

Wings—None
Body—Gold tinsel
Legs—Blue dun game cock hackle, long
Tail—Few barbs as hackle
Hook—No. 11 Hardy

Grey Fox Variant

Wings—None
Body—Gold tinsel
Legs—Ginger game cock, with grizzled cock hackle worked in as front hackle, long
Tail—Ginger cock barbs
Hook—No. 11 Hardy

Cream Variant or Spider

Wings—None
Body—Silver tinsel
Legs—Cream game cock, long
Tail—Cream cock barbs
Hook—No. 11 Hardy

Spiders are often tied on short-shanked hooks, but it has been the experience of the writer that too many fish are lost, on account of the lack of leverage in setting the hook, and it is suggested that a hook as recommended be used. Very small hooks are often found on commercial flies of the Spider or Variant type, and the reason for using them is that good hackle is difficult to obtain and poor hackle will not support the proper size hook on the water; hence, the small hook. Good hackle and a fairly large hook are essential for the successful Variant type of fly.

While the Royal Coachman Fan-wing is not in the strictest sense a Variant, but a fancy pattern not representative of any particular natural fly, it is often a very killing pattern, and it is therefore included here. The dressing of the Royal Coachman is so familiar that it will not be given. Sometimes it is difficult to find the proper feather for dressing the Fan-wing. The best feather for forming the wings of the Fan-wing Royal Coachman is the breast feather of the mandarin drake. Two feathers of the same curvature should be selected, otherwise the fly is likely to spin when cast and twist up the leader.

STREAMERS AND BUCKTAILS

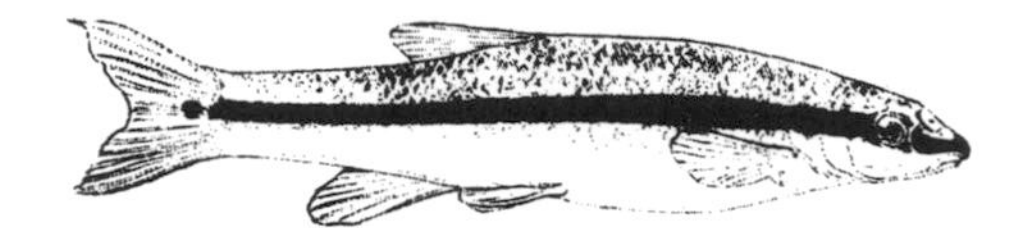

1. *Rhinichthys atronsus*, Black nosed Dace

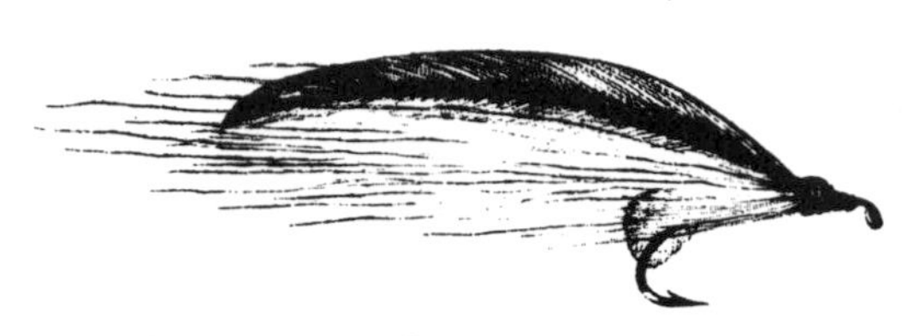

2. Bucktail

3. Polar Bear

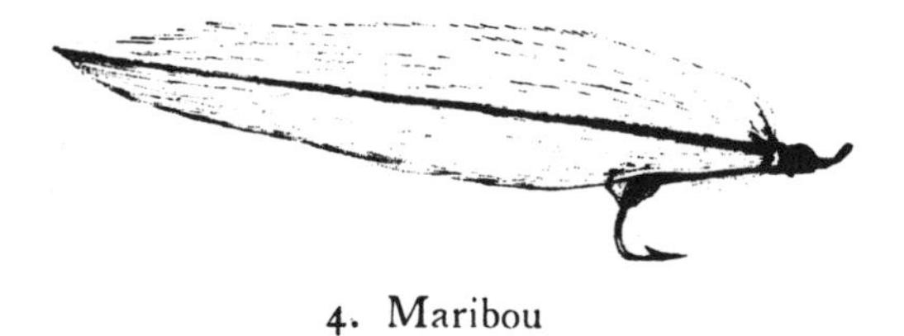

4. Maribou

CHAPTER III

Minnows

Natural minnows are used by a great many native fishermen in the Catskill Mountain region, and many is the big trout that has fallen victim to their seductive flirt, spun in the expert manner of the native fisherman out for a mess of fish.

The streams of the Catskills are not especially productive of fly life, and for that reason trout have to depend on minnows and other small fish for a large part of their food.

The larger a trout grows, the more food it requires; hence minnows become a necessary part of their diet, after the trout reaches a size of ten inches.

The particular minnow which seems to appeal to the appetite of the Catskill trout is a small one, measuring about two and one-half inches in length, and having a dark stripe down the side; this minnow is called a Black Nosed Dace. It is known scientifically as *Rhinichthys atronsus Mitchell.*

The Black Nosed Dace reaches a length of three inches, but those of two and one-half inches are preferred by most fishermen, as they cast easier than the larger specimens and are not such a strain on a light fly rod.

The report of the Commissioner of Fisheries for the State of New York, year 1900, has a complete description of this minnow, and a few of the most interesting observations are as follows: "Color, blackish above; some of the scales irregularly darker; a black band passing from the snout, through the eye and alongside the body, a paler streak below it; belly, silvery; males in the Spring with a lateral band, scarlet or orange; the red color growing fainter later in the season."

The writer is not a bait-fisherman, not because he has any particular prejudice against bait-fishing in general, but because he is of the opinion that it is a lot more fun trying to fool a wise old trout with an artificial fly than by mixing up a lot of snaggle hooks with his lunch—and, to be perfectly honest, minnows are too hard to catch.

The best representations of the natural minnow are the artificial flies known as Bucktails and Streamers. Both of these flies should be used without a spinner, and should be manipulated by the fisherman to represent a minnow.

These flies are large and are readily visible to the fish, which is an important item especially in the early Spring when the streams are high and the water roiled.

Just when these flies were first used is difficult to say, but the Bucktail has come into prominence in the Catskills since the Esopus has been kept in an almost constant roily state, by the introduction of the clay-laden water from the Schoharie; in fact, the first one of these flies to come to the attention of the writer was called the Esopus Bucktail. In any case the Bucktail and the Streamer are both successful in cloudy and roily water.

Many authors of books on trout-fishing have voiced their opinions as to the correct size of fly to use in relation to the state of the water, but none of them has put it in quite the clear and concise manner of W. C. Stewart, author of THE PRACTICAL ANGLER published in 1857. Stewart says: "The two great causes which should regulate the angler in selecting the size of the fly to be used are the colour and size of the water, and the wariness of the trout; the fly, in fact, *must be large enough to ensure it being seen, but not so large as to enable the trout to detect its artificial character.*"

During high and discolored water, Stewart used live minnows and the tails of small parr salmon; but I am sure that he would have used a Streamer fly or a Bucktail if such a fly had been available at that time.

The Streamer fly is usually tied on a normal length hook, size six or eight; two cock hackles are tied to the top of the hook shank to represent the body of the minnow. A dark badger hackle, which has a white or yellow ground with a black stripe in the center, is ideal for the Black Nosed Dace. A Plymouth Rock hackle may also be used, in case the badger hackle is not available.

The hook shank is usually wound with silver or gold tinsel to give a flash when the fly is drawn through the water. Two small jungle cock feathers are sometimes used for the same purpose, these feathers being tied in at the head of the fly.

The Bucktail is usually tied on a long shank hook, size four or six, but the writer's preference is number eight Allcock No. 6827 Salmon Fly Hook; this hook is just about right for a fly two and one-half inches long.

The bucktail is bunched and tied on top of the hook shank, as in the case of the Streamer fly, the hook shank having been first covered with tinsel. Incidentally, in case regular treated tinsel specially prepared for fly-tying purposes is not available, it is advisable to paint the tinseled hook shank with ordinary finger-nail polish; this prevents the tinsel from tarnishing.

A few strands of brown hair from a bucktail or two black cock hackles are then tied on top of the bunched bucktail, these representing the stripe on the side of the minnow, and are desirable features of the Bucktail. Jungle cock feathers may also be added if desired.

Some anglers recommend the use of polar bear hair instead of using bucktail, and this is very fine material as the polar bear is a water-loving animal and his hair is practically waterproof, and has a beautiful glossy sheen. The writer has used polar bear hair for some time and believes it to be superior to any other type of hair used in tying minnow type flies. However, it is rather difficult to obtain.

Maribou, which has been used for a number of years in the construction of certain lures for bass, has recently been adapted for use in Streamer flies. Maribou is a soft feather and wets easily, and being responsive to the action of the water, has a nice action. Like most large flies, however, it has a reputation for raising trout, but very often it is refused, because the fish detects the fraud.

In fishing this type of fly in the Catskill streams it is customary to wade downstream and cast across in the direction of the far bank, retrieving the fly in short jerks, as the fly is swept downstream with the current. At the end of the cast, or when the fly is directly downstream below the fisherman, the fly may be still further retrieved in short jerks and then be allowed to settle back with the current again, in the same manner that one imagines a minnow might do when too tired to keep up the struggle against the current.

A fairly heavy leader is recommended, as the trout hit this type of fly with a great deal of vigor, just as though they were allowed "one strike and out," and in taking natural minnows this is probably often true, as the minnow is well equipped with swimming gear and uses it to good advantage. Flies and Nymphs are not so well equipped with means of locomotion, and are taken by trout in much more leisurely fashion.

A 1x tapered leader of about nine feet has proven satisfactory to the writer when using a rather soft action rod, but a still heavier leader is recommended for use with a heavy or stiff action rod.

While Streamers and Bucktails are most useful during periods of high and cloudy water, when wet-flies and dry-flies are too small to be readily seen by the trout, they can also be used with some hope of success in clear water, but the writer would suggest that the effort be directed to those parts of the streams known as riffles, since this type of water helps to conceal the fact that the artificial fly is artificial and not a Black Nosed Dace in person.

Brown Trout as a general rule will not take a fly which they have once refused; in other words, if a trout rises to a fly either wet or dry and then refuses to take the fly, we say that the trout has come short, or missed the fly, and it is seldom that they will bother to rise again at the same fly in the immediate future. In the case of the Bucktail or Streamer fly the fact that a trout has refused the fly does not seem to make any difference, as the writer has often risen a trout two or three times in succession before finally hooking him. The reason for this is that a minnow is often crippled and swims erratically and, even though crippled, still has sufficient power of locomotion to dodge; the trout, dashing after the fly which is being manipulated by the angler, often misses it and must think that perhaps that minnow is not so badly crippled after all—and comes for it again the next time that it comes within its vision. So, if you rise a good trout keep right after him and the chances are that you will succeed in hooking him.

PART IV

CHAPTER I

Vision

We will never be able to definitely say with any degree of accuracy just what a trout sees when it examines a fly floating upon the surface of the water. The reason for this is simple—we have no means of communicating with a trout. There is an old saying to the effect that a veterinary has to be a better doctor than the ordinary practitioner because people tell the doctor what is wrong with them, while the veterinary himself has to figure out what is wrong. We are in about the same position as the veterinary when it comes to figuring out the mental reactions of a trout.

Whole books have been written on the subject of the trout and its environment, and it is not the purpose of the writer to dwell upon the very much involved subject of optics and light, except to call attention to the fact that the trout lives in water and, therefore, looks through a denser medium than the air to which we are accustomed. And further, a light ray entering and leaving water always does so at a definite angle of 48½ degrees. These facts have been confirmed by Dr. Francis Ward and so recorded in his books, Animal Life Under Water and The Marvels of Fish Life.

From the above premise we reason first that the vision of

a trout must be comparatively short, water being dense and not so well lighted as the air in which we live. Second, that the trout can see by direct vision objects on the surface of the water, which fall within the limits of a circle representing the base of an inverted cone, the eye of the trout being at the apex. In other words, the trout looks at objects upon the surface of the water in much the same manner in which a man looks through a funnel. This imaginary funnel through which the trout looks is bounded by the rays of light entering the water and striking the eye of the trout, a phenomenon which we call sight or vision. In the trout's case the range of vision is limited to 48½ degrees in any upward direction, as that is the definite angle at which light enters and leaves water.

The size of the imaginary circle which marks the limits of the trout's vision of objects on the surface is governed by the depth of the trout in the water. The deeper the trout is in the water the larger area of surface it can watch by direct vision. Outside of this area of direct vision the trout cannot see anything on the surface of the water unless the surface is indented by the weight of the object resting upon it. In this entire area of indirect vision the light entering the water strikes the stream bed and is reflected to the surface, where it lights the under side of the surface film, forming to all intents a mirror. This mirror reflects the entire under-water world below it, and this world is limited only by the keenness of the trout's vision and the amount of light available.

Flies, either naturals or artificials, floating on the surface of the water indent the surface film because of their weight and these dents collect light in much the same manner a lens does. As far as the fish and its vision is concerned, the fly is just as visible as a lightning bug on a dark night. The trout sees the sparkles of light radiating from the dents in the surface film, and if the pattern of the dents looks as though it might be a fly, the reflexes are stimulated and a rise results. The fly may be refused after closer inspection, but it is the writer's opinion that the impulse to investigate is stimulated long before the fly arrived within the limits of the trout's direct vision.

This is one of the reasons for putting so much stress upon the choice of hackle for dry-flies; the better the quality of hackle the fewer turns necessary to properly float the fly, and the fewer turns the more natural the light impressions made by the artificial floating on the surface.

The weight of the fly has a great deal to do with the character of the light pattern, and lightly dressed flies are to be preferred on that account. Much of the success of the type of flies known as Variants is probably due to the lightness of their construction.

So far the fly is only approaching the trout's window, being carried along by the current. In the trout's mind the desire to rise has been stimulated by the familiar sight of the telltale dents and sparkles of light, which are associated with food. As the fly moves across the border of the imaginary circle which limits the area of direct vision, what does the trout see? Dr. Francis Ward saw from the submarine chamber a fly, wings, legs, body and tail, but does the trout see and interpret a thing in the same manner as a human being? In the humble opinion of the writer the answer is no. The reason for this statement is the fact that man comprehends solids in terms of three dimensions, height, width, and length, while animals, not being able to form concepts, interpret solids in terms of only two dimensions, height and width, or length and width.

We human beings see only the outside of solids, and only two of these dimensions at a time. We visualize the third dimension and carry it in the mind's eye as a concept. In short, we have the mental development which enables us to see things in terms which animals cannot appreciate, because of their inferior mental development. This subject has been handled in a masterly fashion by P. D. Ouspensky, in his book entitled TERTIUM ORGANUM, and anyone interested in pursuing this subject further is referred to this book.

If this general theory in respect to the lack of ability on the part of animals to form concepts is correct, and it has all of the earmarks of being at least reasonable, we can begin to understand why it is that, on certain occasions, trout will take flies which to us appear to have entirely different forms. Take for instance such flies as the following: the Woodruff, a spent-wing fly; the Fan-wing Royal Coachman, a fan-wing fly; the Red Hackle, a simple hackle pattern. All of these flies to our eyes, when seen in reflected light, appear to have different forms; but when viewed against the source of light, and interpreted in the terms of only two dimensions, they evidently all look alike to the trout. Who knows?

Is this seemingly catholic taste on the part of the trout due to its willingness to take a chance and try anything once, or is it due to the fact that the flies actually look so much alike when viewed against the light that they are taken for one pattern?

The writer is inclined to favor the latter theory, and believes that a killing fly may be dressed in any of the three forms mentioned, namely, Spent-wing, Fan-wing or Hackle, provided the proper precaution is taken to conform to the same general outline in terms of two dimensions, when viewed against the light. The same general light transmission through the combined hackle and wings must of course suggest the light-transmitting qualities of the wings and legs of the natural fly which is being imitated.

Trout, like all animals including man, are attracted by movement. However, they are not favorably attracted by any movement which is not natural and will avoid a floating fly that is dragging or moving across the current in an unnatural manner. A Mayfly emerging from the stream usually requires several seconds in which to dry its wings before taking flight, and often the wings are fluttered rapidly before they are sufficiently dry to bear the fly aloft. This movement on or above the surface of the water is visible to the fish immediately below and often a rise is stimulated by this attractive movement on the part of the fly.

Well-chosen hackle on a dry-fly, if it has been selected with the view of suggesting to the trout the shade of coloring as well as the translucency of the natural fly's wings in motion, is probably the high point in the killing quality of any dry-fly.

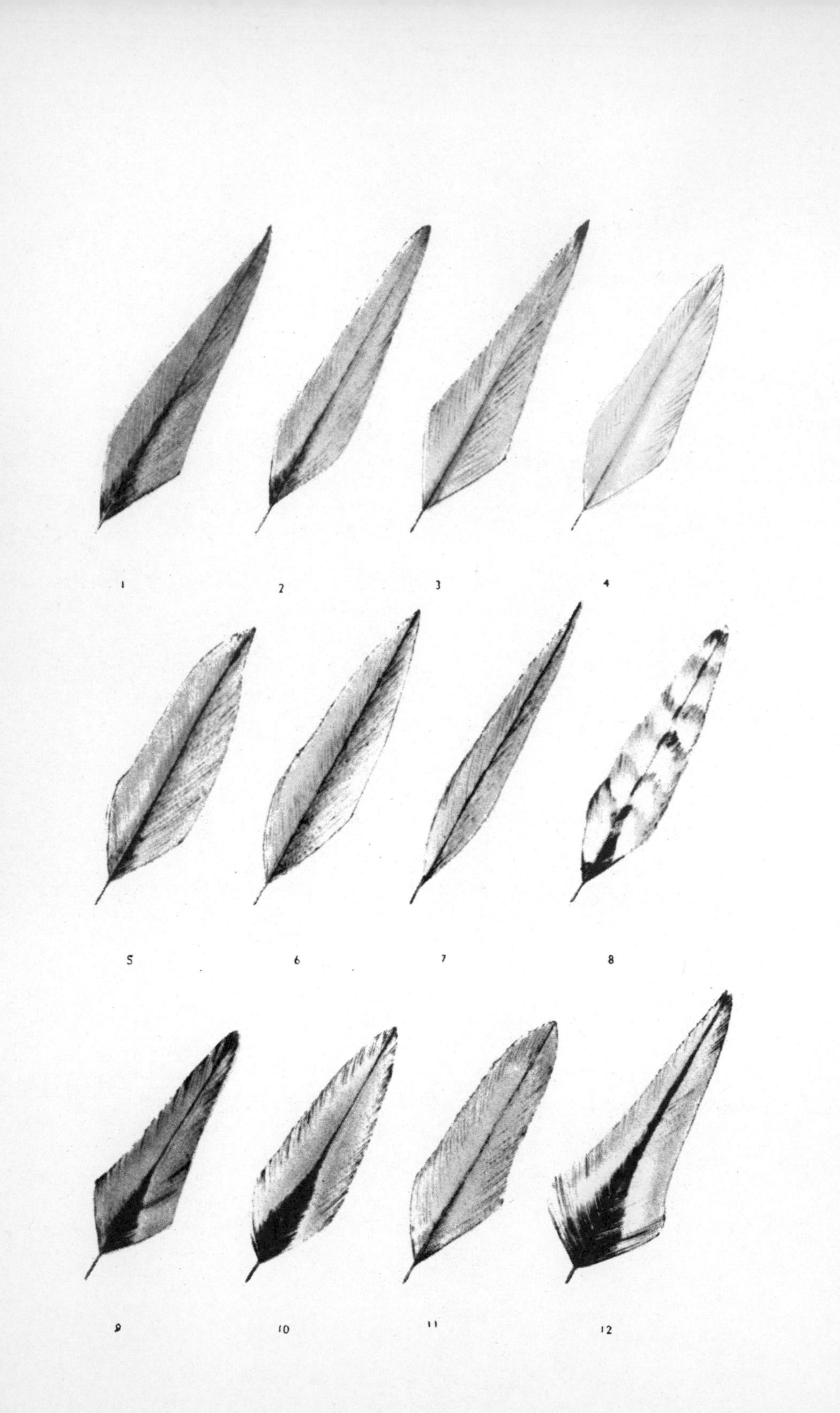
1
2
3
4
5
6
7
8
9
10
11
12

HACKLES

Hackles with a preponderance of red pigment

1. A red hackle from an Old English Game Cock.
2. The same feather as No. 1, showing the reverse side; note that both sides are of approximately the same color.
3. A Ginger Hackle from an American Game Cock. To find this color combined with good shape is not common.
4. Honey. Useful for flies which represent the light colored *Ephemeridae* occurring late in the season.

Hackles with a preponderance of black pigment

5. Dark Blue Dun from an Old English Game Cock. Particularly useful in the tying of the Variant type flies.
6. Light Blue Dun from an Old English Game Cock. This color is rare and a combination of the correct color and good quality is rarer still.
7. Honey Dun from an Old English Game Cock. Has a blue center shading off to a honey color at the tips of the barbs. Used for tying the Coffin Fly.
8. Grizzle Hackle from a Plymouth Rock Cock. A slight tinge of red often indicates the presence of Red Game blood and they are best quality.

Hackles with black and red pigment

9. Furnace. A useful feather for imitating the darker flies.
10. Cochy-bondhu, literally red and black. This feather is similar to the Furnace except that the tips of the barbs are black.
11. Furnace Dun. A variation of the Cochy-bondhu.
12. Badger. Used in the imitation of the small black flies known as Black Gnats.

CHAPTER II

Hackle

ONE of the most important items entering into the construction of a good dry-fly is a well-chosen feather from the neck of a cock, which feather is commonly known as a hackle feather or simply a hackle.

As all types of fowl do not produce hackle feathers suitable for use in the best dry-flies, the object of this chapter is to discuss the different qualities of a good hackle and, if possible, point out the desirable features to be sought.

The use of cock's hackles for the construction of artificial flies is by no means a new thought. The very first written reference to an artificial fly mentions the use of a cock's hackle as being one of the two items necessary to form the fly about the hook. According to authorities on literature, the first reference to an artificial fly being used in fishing occurs in a book entitled NATURAL HISTORY, written sometime during the early part of the Christian Era, by an Italian named Aelian. This book was written in the Greek language and the translation which is given in Mr. O. Lambert's ANGLING LITERATURE IN ENGLAND reads as follows:

"They fasten red wool round a hook and fit on the wool two feathers which grow under a cock's wattles, and which in color are like wax."

This is the original specification for the fly, which even today is known as the Red Palmer or Red Hackle, and the dressing of this fly is the same today as when the lowly Galilean walked beside the still waters. Students of ancient angling literature have pointed out that, while this reference to the artificial fly was first written during the second or third century of the present era, the artificial fly had probably been in use for a number of years, or perhaps centuries, as Aelian speaks of this method of fishing as a more or less established practice and by no means as something novel or new.

The domestic cock, from which the hackle feathers are taken was possibly the object of primitive man's first attempt at husbandry. Just when or how these birds were first tamed is, of course, lost in the maze of generations which have followed since man first domesticated the wild jungle fowl of India, Ceylon, and the Malay Peninsula.

It is not unlikely that the fighting ability of the wild jungle cock attracted the primitive man, and this characteristic was perhaps one of the prime factors which led to its being captured and domesticated. Cock-fighting is one of the principal sports of the Malay Peninsula even today and it is entirely possible that the savage primitive man staged a fight between two rival jungle cocks for the amusement of friends and neighbors. In any case cock-fighting became one of the earliest forms of sports. Now the feathers which grow about the neck and throat of the cock serve a very useful purpose, apart from the ordinary benefits afforded by plumage, and that purpose is to protect the throat from their adversary in battle. In the battle for survival of the fittest, the birds with the best protection survived and were bred for their fighting ability.

There are two distinct breeds of jungle fowl, the Red Jungle Fowl and the Grey Jungle Fowl. The Grey Jungle Fowl do not produce feathers suitable for hackles, but the feather with the paint-like spot, which is so often used in the manufacture of salmon flies, is from this bird. The Red Jungle Fowl is the bird that is of particular interest to the fly-fisher, as this bird is the progenitor of all domestic poultry found in this country as well as England. I mention England for the reason that fly-fishing is highly developed there and most of the flies used in America are either tied in England or else the materials of which the flies are made are imported from England and the flies actually tied here.

From the original Red Jungle Fowl, all the breeds of modern poultry have been developed by selective breeding: the prolific egg producing machines, the Leghorns; the lumbering, plodding Black Giants; and finally, the bird that still has the protective hackle of fine quality, the bird that fights for the sheer love of the fight, the Game Cock.

Without doubt the bird producing the finest hackle in the world for use in the tying of dry-flies is the breed known as the "Old English Game Fowl."

Before the advent of the dry-fly on the fast, rocky streams of the North of England, it was necessary to have a fine grade of hackle to make the standard patterns of wet-flies then in use. The ordinary hackle or hen hackle was useless, as it quickly matted about the hook forming a shapeless mass, which, Dr. Cutcliffe said, "makes your fly look more like a little oval black mass of dirt than a living insect."

Dr. Cutcliffe was one of the first to recognize the value of the Game Cock as a source of hackles, as he says in his excellent little book TROUT FISHING IN RAPID STREAMS, published in 1883, "The best of all fowls for hackles is the Old English Game Cock, which, however, is now very difficult to obtain; no bird seems to have such lustrous shining, stiff and well-shaped feathers as this game fowl, such as was used in times of yore for cock-fighting."

Cock-fighting has been prohibited by law in England since 1850 or thereabouts, but there are still a number of Game Fowl bred for exhibition purposes; in fact, there were nearly 600 birds of the Old English Game variety shown at the Oxford Show in 1934. This is not a lot of chickens in comparison with the number of broilers turned out by some of our large poultry farms; but if someone had let loose those 600 game chickens the ensuing free-for-all would have been "sumpin'."

Cock-fighting in America has also been prohibited by law, but as Game Cocks hold such a high place in the esteem and admiration of the average sportsman a few are still bred by those men whose love for the magnificent has not been killed by legislation.

The American Game Fowl originated from birds probably brought over from England during the Colonial times; in fact, General George Washington was the proud possessor of a fine flock of game chickens. The American Game Cock also produces a fine grade of hackle, but the center rib of the feather seems to be a little coarse when compared with the very best quality hackle from birds bred in England. The difference in the feeding or the climate may have some bearing on this difference in the texture of the feather.

The age of the bird has a great deal to do with the quality of the hackle feathers, the best hackle being obtained when the bird is two years old. Young birds have hackles of poor shape and soft texture, which soak up water readily and for that reason are not the best for dry-flies. After a bird has reached the age of three years, the hackles begin to coarsen in texture, and the barbs of the feather are usually bowed or bent, and the very old birds are to be avoided on that account.

Hackles seem to be at their best during the middle of the Winter, when the rib or center quill is firm and hard. The entire plumage of the bird is usually in prime condition at this time; the number of undeveloped feathers, or pin feathers, is at a minimum. This is the season when most of the older fowl are shipped to the markets in the cities, and this is the time when the hackles used in the tying of commercial trout flies are collected.

A hackle suitable for tying a good dry-fly should be of

a good shape; in other words, the usable part of the feather, after the soft down at the butt end has been stripped off, should be long in the rib, and the barbs which stand off from the rib should be comparatively short. Halford, in describing what he termed a "Perfect Hackle," said that the shape of the hackle should be that of a triangle, the base of which should be one-half the length of the altitude. As the barbs are on both sides of the rib, the ratio between the rib and the barbs would be about four to one. Such a hackle does not exist except in theory; but if there had been some way of making hackle feathers "to order," that is the shape Halford would have selected.

In actual practice the best shaped hackles that have come to the attention of the writer are those from an American Game Cock, and the ratio between the center rib and the barbs is two and one-half to one, which is a long way from the four to one of Halford's "Perfect Hackle." If the barbs be stroked back, so that they stand out at a right angle to the rib, the shape of a good hackle will be found to be rectangular rather than triangular; but this I have found to be no disadvantage, as the hackles with barbs of uniform length work up nicely, and are to be preferred in tying the large Spider or Variant type flies.

Good cock hackles should be springy, the barbs standing off at right angles to the central rib when the rib is bent between the fingers. The feather should snap back into position, when released after bending. The outer surface of the feather should be glassy and shining, glistening when examined in the bright light. The barbs should be clear and translucent, and of nearly the same color on both sides.

Game fowl that have come to America from the Malay States do not appear to have as fine a quality of hackle as the birds that have come to us by the way of England. One of the best known breeds of American poultry, the Rhode Island Red, is the result of a cross with a Malay Game Cock which was brought home on a sailing ship many years ago. The Rhode Island Red has a hackle of good color on the outer side, but the under side is of a dirty brown color, and the texture of the feather is chalky, rather than of the fine steely hardness which characterizes the feather from the Old English Game Fowl.

Only two color pigments are found in the feathers of domestic fowl, according to no less an authority than Dr. M. A. Jull, of the United States Department of Agriculture, in an article which appeared in April, 1927, issue of *National Geographic Magazine*. All feathers from domestic birds, no matter of what color or shade, contain only red pigment or black pigment, or combinations of these two pigments. The difference in the color of any two feathers is due to the amount of pigment present, and to the arrangement of the pigment granules within the structure of the feather. Artists tell us that black pigment never enters into combination with another pigment to form a third pigment of a different color, such as red pigment and blue pigment combining to form purple pigment, and that the black pigment always retains its identity; in short, it will not blend, it only mixes. Mention is made of this for the reason that due to the scarcity of hackles of desirable colors, commercial manufacturers of flies often have to resort to the use of dyes. The effect is often disappointing, as the dyes are made up of flat colors, and, of course, the feather is dyed an equally flat color, while the color of the natural feather, being a mixture of two pigments, presents a more lifelike appearance. For this and other reasons dyed materials, and especially feathers, are to be avoided when possible.

The desirable colors of hackle for use in tying the standard patterns of dry-flies are: all of the feathers which contain red pigment in preponderance, such as, bright red, ginger, honey, and cream. The hackles which contain black pigment in preponderance, such as, the blue black hackle from the Blue Andalusian cock—which bird incidentally does not produce a very good grade of hackle—ranging to the blue duns, dark and light, down to the honey dun. The dun feathers appear to be blue, but there is usually a good deal of red pigment present, which can be seen when the feather is held against the light. This does not detract in any way; in fact, it is a decided advantage. The grizzled hackles, from birds having a strain of the Plymouth Rock breed in them, are also useful. Feathers containing both red and black pigment in fairly equal amounts are known as furnace, flame, and the lighter shades, as badgers. The cochy-bondhu is similar to the furnace, except the tips of the barbs are black.

Probably the color most sought is the one known as the

light blue dun; this hackle is necessary for the tying of two of the most popular patterns of dry-flies used in the East. This same color of hackle is also used in England to tie one of the most popular flies used in the North of England, the Blue Upright, and to all intents and purposes is similar to our Quill Gordon, except that the duck flank feather wings are omitted. Game fowl which produce this hackle have been bred in England for some years, and the breed is known as the Old English Blue Dun Games.

There are still a few breeders in England who raise these birds, but the price asked puts them out of the reach of the average fisherman. However, on occasion one of these birds finds its way into the market, and some fly-fisher with an eye for quality buys it and gets a lot of fine hackles; but, alas, this happens only too seldom.

Blue Games can also be produced by crossing a pure white cock with a black hen, and it is not unlikely that the first of the blue strains were originated in this manner. The cost of maintaining a flock of chickens, especially game chickens, is considerable, and could be undertaken only by someone who had the proper facilities for taking care of them. The writer's suggestion to anyone interested in breeding blue fowl for hackles, is to hunt up some friend who is interested in game fowl and have him undertake the actual breeding and rearing of these birds, as the additional revenue from the hackles, which are usually thrown away, should be welcome, and the cost of the hackles kept at a minimum.

Hackles from the saddle region are nice to look at but they are of little use in tying the best dry-flies, because the central rib is often too weak to provide proper support for the barbs. However, saddle hackles are useful in tying wet-flies, as the weak rib allows the barbs to move freely in the water, which is a desirable consideration in a wet-fly, but a decided detriment in a dry-fly which needs good, firm, well planted legs for support.

Hen hackles are useless for the ordinary patterns of dry-flies, as the barbs are too weak to properly support the weight of the hook. There are some types of flies where this kind of hackle can be used to advantage, such as Spent Mayflies which lie prone on the surface film of the stream. In this type of fly the hackle is not intended to support the fly above the surface of the water, but allows it to sink into the surface film, in the same manner a natural Spent May-fly floats. The hen hackle, being soft, sinks into the water and moves about with every influence of the current.

Most of the dressed poultry that appears in our markets has been plucked of all feathers, but in the case of capons a few feathers are sometimes left, possibly to indicate that the bird had been plucked dry and not scalded before plucking. These hackles are often sold to the uninitiated as cock's hackles, while as a matter of fact they are not cock's hackles at all. The capon would have been a cock had he not been deprived of his organs of reproduction, and it is a well-known fact that a bird in this state will assume the plumage characteristics of the female; hence the capon's hackles are

A PURE WHITE GAME COCK

PHOTOS BY WILLIS K. STAUFFER

A RED GAME COCK, WITH HACKLES ERECT

usually coarse and soft and better adapted for wet-flies than dry-flies. Ancient fly-fishers recognized the soft structure of the capon's hackle and its suitability for use on wet-flies. As a matter of fact, the venerable Dame Juliana Berners (1496) speaks highly of her flies tied with "Redde Capons Hakyll."

Cock's hackles of a fine quality are exceedingly difficult to obtain, and the writer has no suggestions to offer as to where they are to be found. Someone has likened them to gold—it is where you find it. However, he would suggest that once a source of supply is found, a good store of hackles be collected as they do not deteriorate rapidly. Moths are very fond of expensive feathers, but a heavy sprinkling of camphor flakes or other insect repellent should keep them away.

CHAPTER III

WINGS

THE first dry-flies to come to the attention of the American fly-fisher were doubtless the winged flies of the English chalk streams. Mary Orvis Marbury, in her book FAVORITE FLIES, published in 1892, shows a plate of 15 dry-flies selected from those currently in use in England. All of the flies shown were winged with either starling wing feathers or wing feathers from other birds.

Emlyn M. Gill in PRACTICAL DRY-FLY FISHING, published in 1912, and G. M. L. LaBranche in DRY-FLY AND FAST WATER, published in 1914, have a leaning towards flies tied with wings of starling. This was also due to the influence of the English dry-fly fishers, who were very active on the chalk streams during this period.

There has been a growing tendency during recent years, both among the professional as well as the amateur fly-tyers of America, to omit the wings from dry-flies. This tendency has been encouraged by several considerations, the first being the fact that flies winged with starling or duck wing feathers easily become frayed and mussed. There was a time when a fly-fisher would discard a fly after taking a fish, but since the lean years have arrived old flies are not discarded; they are carefully stroked back into their original shape and used again and again. The second consideration which has encouraged the use of the hackle or palmer fly, is the fact that wings made of feathers from birds' wing quills are not easy to tie, in fact more time can be wasted over the "set" of a pair of starling wings than would ordinarily be consumed in the tying of several flies.

For fine clear waters, and especially on still pools, an exact copy, or one as nearly exact as is possible to make, is often desirable, and an artificial winged with the wing quill feathers of starling may be used to advantage. The natural flies occupying these still pools are, as a general rule, small in size, and the wings may well be represented by slips of feather taken from the best primary feather of a starling's wing. On these still pools a trout has ample time to inspect the fly and, if there are naturals on the water, a good copy of the natural should bring results if properly presented. Most of the small light flies, such as the Ginger Quill and Little Marryat, are tied with starling wings. In selecting a feather from the wing of a starling the first primary should be discarded, as this feather is stiff and the fibres tend to separate easily. The second, third and fourth primaries are the best for dry-flies; the secondary feathers may be used for small wet-flies.

For the darker colored flies, such as Greenwell's Glory, or the Iron Blue Dun, the writer knows of no feather that quite takes the place of the English hen blackbird. These birds are of the thrush family and do not belong to the same family as the American blackbird. They are killed for the markets in England and the wings may be obtained from the tackle dealers.

For flies such as the American March Brown and the Grey Fox, the flank feather of a mallard drake is recommended. It is probable that the upright split-wing dry-fly, tied with the flank feather of mallard or wood-duck, was the invention of Theodore Gordon, the Quill Gordon dry-fly being typical of this class. In selecting feathers from the flank of a mallard drake only the strongest feathers, which usually occur only on old birds, should be selected, and the feathers which are listed by the dealers as Mediums are to be preferred as they have the flue or barbs of the feather distributed evenly on both sides of the central rib. This allows the use of one feather to form both wings of the fly.

For the Quill Gordon, Hendrickson and Light Cahill dry-flies, the flank feather of a mandarin drake is recommended. This feather is slightly browner in shade than the feather from the American wood-duck which was formerly used by fly-tyers. The wood-duck is now protected by law, and every sportsman should see that protection is actually afforded these beautiful birds. The wood-duck is the handsomest bird living in America today, and the few which have survived the shotguns of fly-tyers should certainly be given a chance to breed in security, and, for a little while at least, not to go the way of the heath hen, the passenger pigeon and the dodo.

Wings of dry-flies formed of the flank feather from a duck are most useful on the medium-sized flies, especially when they are used on flies which represent those naturals which seem to sit low on the water. The bunches of speckled fibres of the duck flank feather not only suggest the cross-veining of the natural fly's wings but, looking at the fly from the front, as the trout often sees it on the water, the two dense masses of duck feather, surrounded by the sparse hackle, must suggest motion, and provide a mental stimulus for the trout to seize it before it gets away.

For the Fan-wing Royal Coachman no better feather has been found than the breast feather of the mandarin drake, and again the quality of the feather is most important, the old birds' being best. The feathers from that area of the breast just below the shoulder are the best shaped for the wings of the Fan-wing, as they have the best curvature of rib. In selecting feathers for Fan-wings, take both wings from the same location on the bird; otherwise, the fly will not balance properly.

For wet-flies, coot wings are suggested, as these feathers are easy to work and have a wide range of color, from slate to light grey. The writer prefers coot to duck wing quills, as the coot are softer and, because of their flexibility, respond to the action of the current. This latter feature is a desirable quality in all feathers which are to be used as wings for wet-flies.

For the wet Coachman and Royal Coachman, no feather quite comes up to the standards of swan wing quills. These feathers are easy to work and are remarkably fine in texture.

WINGS

For the wings of the Caddis or Sedge flies, which are usually fished as wet-flies, a feather from the wing of a bittern is suggested. This feather has the mottled markings which are typical of the larger types of Sedge flies, especially those which emerge during August, and in addition has the desirable qualities of strength and flexibility. Bustard has been used successfully as a wing for the Sedge flies, but as this feather is very soft and perishable, the bittern wing feather is preferred. The bittern is a night-feeding bird and it is possible that its feathers have some particular charm on that account. In any case, it is an excellent feather to use in imitating the late-season Sedges, which, incidentally, are night-emerging flies.

CHAPTER IV

Body Materials

Materials for the bodies of flies are comparatively easy to obtain. If hackles and wings were equally easy to get in quantities there would be no excuse for anyone fishing with an inferior fly.

As cheaply as good body material may be obtained, still the great majority of flies in use are tied with materials entirely unsuited to the purpose.

Most of the flies tied for the general commercial trade have bodies made of either silk or wool, neither of which materials is especially good for dry flies, because silk discolors when wet, and wool soaks up water like a sponge.

Wet-flies have been in use for at least nineteen hundred years, and many of the early patterns were tied with wool. When dry-flies became popular the old wet patterns were tied as dry-flies without any change being made in body materials. In almost any tackle shop you can see old Brook Trout patterns of wet-flies tied as dry-flies; for instance, the Montreal and Parmachene Belle, to say nothing of the Grizzly King or the Reuben Wood. Professional fly-tyers have been equally guilty in this respect, as it is much easier to work with a nice ball of wool of the approximate color —dyed of course—than it is to mix up the fur dubbing to the proper shade; but therein lies the art of fly-tying.

Fur from the belly of a red fox is one of the best materials for the bodies of many excellent dry-flies. The Light Cahill and the Hendrickson, two of the most popular patterns of dry-flies used on the Eastern streams, when properly tied, have their bodies composed of the belly fur of a red fox.

Furs, in general, are particularly translucent when wet, and if due precautions are taken in the selection of the proper shade of fur, as well as the proper color tying silk, almost all of the desired effects may be obtained.

Most wild animals have their belly regions much lighter in color than the rest of their bodies. The reason for this is the fact that their belly regions are lighted by the indirect light reflected from the ground over which the animal is standing, while the rest of their bodies is lighted by the stronger direct light. The indirect light is colored by the character of the ground, and the light colored fur on the belly of the animal reflects this colored light, thus blending the lower part of their body with the ground, while their upper regions fit in with the character of their habitat.

Long before Izaak Walton thought of writing THE COMPLEAT ANGLER, one Colonel Venables made an observation which will bear repeating here: "In making the artificial fly, chiefly observe the belly of the fly, for that color the fish most take notice of, as being most in their eye." (EXPERIENCED ANGLER, 1622.)

The bellies of aquatic insects are also designed by nature to be lighted by the indirect light reflected by and colored by the stream bed, and in trying to imitate these natural insects, fur of the proper texture from the belly regions of an animal seems to be the proper thing to use. In actual practice this line of reasoning has been proven to be correct.

If an aquatic animal could be found with fur of the proper color and texture, no doubt this would be superior to the belly fur of a red fox; but as no such animal has been found, we have to be content with the red fox, a land animal.

Muskrat as well as water rat have been used on some of the darker flies, but in general the writer prefers quill from a peacock shoulder feather, when imitating the darker flies.

Seal, both natural and dyed, has its place in the fly-tyer's kit, as it is a hard glossy fur, and, while it is rather intractable alone, it blends nicely with other furs, such as the hare's ear. One of the popular patterns of flies used in England, the Tup's Indispensable, owes a great deal of its coloring to dyed seal's fur. The ruddy seal's fur is mixed with the wool from the indispensable portion of a tup's (ram's) anatomy, forming the basis for the body of this famous fly. This is the only superior dry-fly, to my knowledge, in which wool is used, and this fly is not, in the strictest sense, a dry-fly as it is usually fished semi-submerged to suggest the spent spinner of the Olive Dun lying in the surface film of the placid chalk stream. But even in this instance the wool composing the body is taken from the belly regions of the animal.

Hare's ear, or, strictly speaking, the fur from the poll,

and particularly from between the ears, of an English hare, is an excellent body material as it blends with almost any fur and renders stiff and hard furs more workable. Alone it is also an excellent material for the bodies of Nymphs, or wet-flies which suggest Nymphs.

For some of the light-bodied small flies which appear during June, the flank of an Australian opossum is suggested. This fur is fairly fine in texture and works up nicely; the color is a yellowish-tan. The original dressing of the Little Marryat dry-fly calls for this fur.

For the Quill Gordon and other similar flies, the bicolor quill stripped from the shoulder feather of a peacock is needed. There has been considerable discussion as to where the particular bicolor quills may be found, and a word on this subject may not be amiss. Select the largest peacock feather or plume to be found, and examine the underside of the barbs which go to make up the eye-part of the feather; it will be found that some of these barbs have herl or flue on only one side. If one of these barbs be selected and stripped of the herl, it will be found to be lighter on one-half its width than it is on the other. The stripped quill may be soaked overnight in a bottle of peroxide to bleach the lighter portion of the quill, while the darker portion will remain unchanged in color. When this quill is wound on the hook to form the body of the fly, the alternate bands of light and dark give an attractive and lifelike effect.

Some of the Variant type dry-flies are also tied with quill bodies. In this type of fly the body is elevated so far above the surface of the water that, if the body is seen at all by the fish, it is lighted by direct light rather than indirect light and, therefore, the quill suggests the lateral marking found along the sides of so many of the larger Ephemeral flies.

Gold or silver tinsel is also used for the bodies of some flies, and this material may be purchased from a tackle dealer. Particular precautions should be taken to see that it has been treated to prevent tarnish.

WET-FLIES

1. Early Brown Stone Fly

2. American March Brown

3. Quill Gordon

4. American Alder

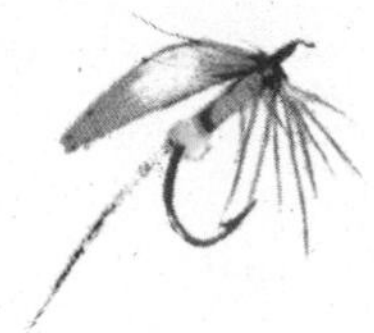

5. Lady Beaverkill

6. Royal Coachman

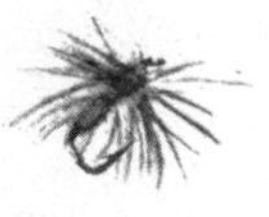

7. Brown Ant

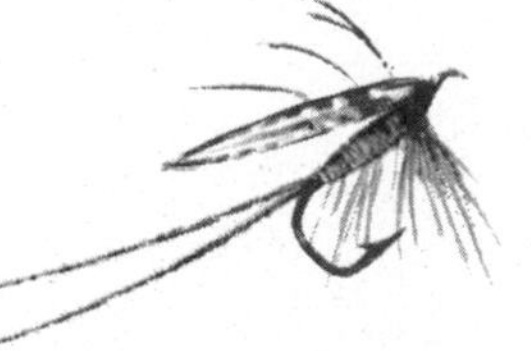

8. Stone Fly Creeper

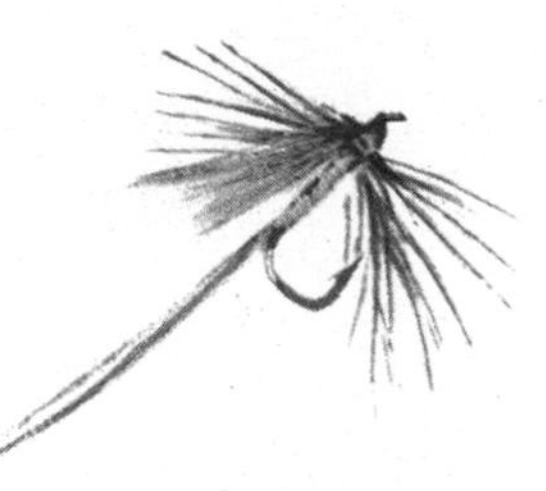

9. Mallard Quill

10. Brown Sedge

11. Leadwing Coachman

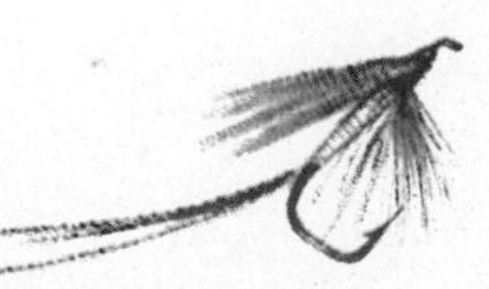

12. Light Cahill

CHAPTER V

TAILS

TAILS on wet-flies have been thought by some of the old writers on angling to be unnecessary, and it is entirely probable that the tail may be dispensed with on wet-flies, as the body is the important consideration. However, in case of the dry-fly the tail is a very important item, not only because it adds to the attractiveness of the fly, but because it assists in floating it in a natural position.

The Mayflies or *Ephemeridae* have two or three tails, but in the artificial fly a half-dozen tail fibres may be used without any apparent effect on the killing qualities of the fly. A dry-fly is a combination of compromises: the body is often much shorter than the body of the natural fly; the wings may be exaggerated, as in the case of the Fan-wing flies, or wings may be only suggested by the use of hackle, all of which detract from the theory of exact imitation but improve the floating and wearing qualities of the pattern being tied.

Barbs from the hackle feathers which guard the throat area of the game cock are in the writer's opinion the best material for the tails of dry-flies. The spade feathers from the shoulder of the cock are finer in quality and are very well suited for the smaller patterns of flies.

A few well-chosen fibres from the flank feather of a male duck are used by some professionals to suggest the speckled tails occurring on some of the early Mayflies, such as the *Ephemerella;* but barbs of cock hackle give better support to the fly and are to be preferred on that account.

For wet-flies a soft, soppy feather is desirable for tails, and a few strands of the fibres from a pheasant's tail feather is suggested as being excellent material for this purpose.

CHAPTER VI

Hooks

Fish hooks are probably the most ancient of all the angler's equipment. Primitive fish hooks in the form of small stones, sharpened at both ends, which were apparently used as gorge hooks, have been found in the peat-beds of France imbedded in the peat twenty-two feet below the surface. Scientists have estimated the time elapsed in forming these layers of peat as ranging between seven thousand and thirty thousand years.

In the book of Job, in the Old Testament, probably written about the year 1520 B.C., the following reference is noted: "Canst thou draw out leviathan with an hook?" which would indicate that the method of fishing with a hook was in ordinary use at least three thousand four hundred years ago. It is a far cry from the prehistoric bit of stone, which was used as a gorge, to the delicate modern fly hook on which the floating fly is tied.

Halford states that the eyed hook which he adopted for the dry-fly was probably the greatest single contributing factor towards the popularization of the sport of dry-fly fishing, as the fly could be changed with the minimum of fuss. Eyed hooks had been in use for some years prior to the dry-fly becoming popular. Mr. Hewett Wheatley in his book published in 1849, entitled Rod and Line, says:

"I generally use them made on hooks having a fine eye at the extremity of the shank. In fact, I very commonly make all flies, large and small, on similar hooks. . . . It possesses the advantage of enabling me to use either fine or thick gut with the same fly. . . . Besides in an ordinary round snuff-box I carry to the river 300 flies."

Today both dry- and wet-flies are generally tied on eyed hooks, for, in addition to the ease with which eyed hooks may be carried, they have the added advantage of durability, as flies tied directly to gut snells often have to be discarded because of the age and brittleness of the gut.

Fish hooks are manufactured in many countries, but it is the writer's experience that British hooks are better adapted for fly-tying than those made in other countries, which often have the fault of being poorly tempered or of having badly formed eyes. While it is not the intention of the writer to endorse any particular brand of hook to the exclusion of all others, in all justice it must be said that the Hardy fly hook meets all of the requirements as set down by Mr. C. Pennell in his book, MODERN PRACTICAL ANGLER. Mr. Pennell lists the following points as being desirable:

1. A searching point
2. Quick penetration without tendency to rake
3. Good holding power
4. Strength
5. Neatness and adaptability to form a fly

In the opinion of the writer the Hardy fly hook meets all of these requirements, as it is so designed as to have an extra wide gape, as well as a slightly snecked point, which tend towards sure hooking. The point, while it is very sharp, is short and is in line with the general direction of the pull of the line, ensuring quick penetration. The barb is heavy, ensuring good holding power.

The wire from which these hooks are made is of the finest quality cast steel, specially drawn for making these fine wire hooks, and the calibre of the wire is in keeping with the size of the hook. The Hardy fly hook is neat in appearance and is of the correct proportion to accommodate properly the dressing of most common flies.

For flies of the fan-wing type, or for the large Green Drake, it is necessary to have a hook with an exceptionally wide gape, such as the Hardy-Emery Mayfly hook.

For some of the wet-flies, especially those with bulky bodies, a heavier hook is needed to get the fly below the surface quickly. For these flies the writer would suggest Bartlett's B 7362. This hook is good and stout, with a square bend which permits of the dressing of flies with long bodies. In the small sizes it is an excellent hook for the small-winged dry-flies, such as the Little Marryat. This hook is much used in England; in fact, it is the favorite hook of that great chalk stream fly-fisher, Mr. G. E. M. Skues. It runs smaller in size than the corresponding number of other hooks, a No. 6 Bartlett B 7362 being the equivalent of a No. 8 Hardy.

For Bucktails and Streamers, Allcock's Salmon Fly hook No. 6827 is ideal. It is a fairly short hook, but as trout usually strike a minnow near the head, it gets the fish. There are times when a Streamer is refused or missed, but in cases where the fly is actually touched by the fish, the chances of hooking are much better when a short-shanked hook is used.

The writer has become very suspicious of the needle-point hooks, for the reason that their points are so long and fine that the slightest contact with the rod in casting results in either a bent or a broken point. Light, long leaders and a windy day are the ideal combination for bending up the points of hooks, and that is one reason for preferring a hook with a short point.

Flies of the Spider or Variant type are often tied on short-shanked hooks, and while this may be all right with a soft hackle, a stiff hackle, which is the best hackle for these flies, seems to interfere with the proper hooking qualities of these hooks and the writer avoids them on that account. With fine gut, the leverage in setting the hook is pretty poor, especially if the line of pull is not in line with the point of the hook, and it seems that in many cases these hooks tend to rake instead of penetrate.

For dry-flies, the weight of the hook is an important consideration and every book on fly-tying recommends the use of a light hook; but there is one thing which is not told and that is what a hook actually weighs. The writer, being curious, weighed some hooks and found that the Hardy fly hook size No. 11, the size perhaps most commonly used, weighed just thirty milligrams. He then tried to ascertain the weight of some of the most common Mayflies, but could not locate anyone who had any information on this subject. Finally, Dr. Paul Needham, who has been conducting some experiments in Fresh Water Biology at Leland Stanford University, advised that the larger aquatic insects would run between forty and fifty milligrams. It would therefore appear that a large fly of the Variant or Spider type can be dressed on a fairly large hook and still keep within the weight of the natural fly.

CHAPTER VII

TOOLS AND SUNDRIES

THE tools for fly-tying are few and simple: a vise, a couple of pairs of hackle pliers, two pairs of scissors and a bodkin are about all that are necessary to turn out excellent flies.

The vise should hold the hook firmly and at the same time cover both the point and the barb, so that the tying silk will not be inadvertently cut. It is not the purpose to advertise any particular model of vise, but the writer has found the Thompson vise well suited to his needs.

The hackle pliers should be of the type known as "Bull-dog Artery Clamps." These clamps may be obtained from almost any dealer in fly-tying supplies, or may be obtained from any store dealing in hospital supplies. The clamps come in various degrees of strength, and it is advisable to select a pair with a strong grip for winding hackles, and a second pair with a weak grip for holding the tying silk. A wooden clamp clothes-pin, with the edges of the jaws filed to a perfect fit, is an ideal plier for holding the tying silk.

The fly-tyer should have at least two pairs of scissors, one for cutting wire, tinsel, etc., and the other pair, which should have fine curved blades, should be reserved for cutting furs and feathers, where a keen edge is necessary for good work.

A bodkin, or a heavy darning needle with a suitable handle, comes in handy at times, especially when finishing off the head of the fly with an invisible knot.

Sundries

Tying Silk. Pearsall's is the recognized standard in tying silks, and it is both strong and fine in gauge. Practically all colors for fly-tying are available. When flies with fur bodies are being tied, it is absolutely necessary to take due regard of the color of the tying silk, as furs are translucent when wet and the tying silk, which is not visible when the fly is dry, shows through the fur when it is wet. Of course, the color of the tying silk is not important when the body of the fly is being made of some opaque material, such as quill or tinsel, when silk of any color may be used.

Wax. For the light flies, a transparent wax is almost a necessity. This may be obtained from any dealer in fly-tying materials. This wax has a tendency to dry out quickly and become hard and brittle, and for that reason the writer is inclined to favor using varnish on the tying silk, although varnish is apt to darken the lighter shades of silk.

Varnish. Varnish is necessary for finishing off the head of the fly after the silk has been tied with an invisible knot. Copal varnish, which may be obtained from any art shop, is excellent, as it penetrates deeply; the only fault that the writer has found with it is the fact that it takes twenty-four hours to dry. Varnish is also used to "wax" the tying silk; this is done as follows: lay the tying silk across the mouth of the open varnish bottle, then cover the silk and the bottle mouth with a finger and invert the bottle; draw silk through the liquid varnish and allow to dry a few seconds before using. The varnish on the finger should be removed with a cloth dampened with varnish remover before proceeding with the tying of the fly.

Ordinary clear lacquer, such as is used for finger-nail polish, is an excellent medium for cementing fan-wings into position, and the writer would suggest that a bottle of this material be kept on hand for this purpose.

Brushes. In applying varnish and lacquer, some tyers use a small sable brush. If a brush is to be used be sure to get one suitable for use with oil paints and not one designed for water colors, as the latter is too soft. A sliver of bamboo, whittled to a sharp point, is about as good an instrument as has come to the attention of the writer for applying varnish to the head of a fly. The bamboo is hard and is easily cleaned.

Tinsel and Wire. Both tinsel and fine wire should be obtained from the fly-tying material dealer, and special precautions taken to ensure its having been treated to prevent tarnish; otherwise, a fly tied of excellent materials may be spoiled by the tarnishing of the tinsel or wire.

FLY-TYING AND HOOKS

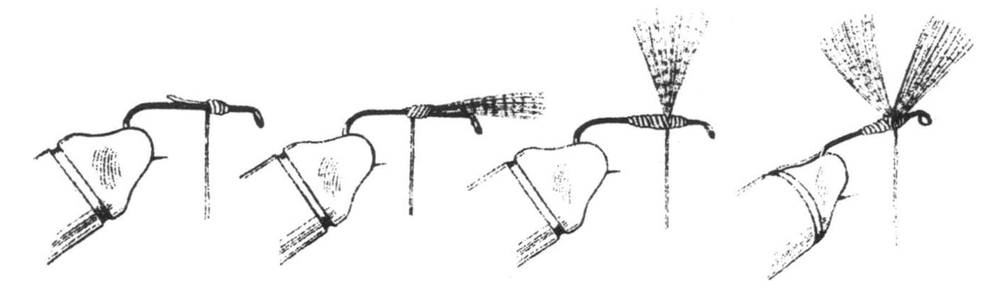

1. Tying duck flank feather wing

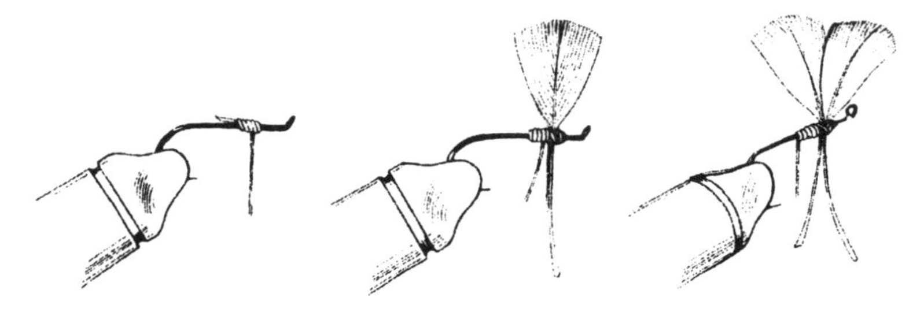

2. Tying Fan-wings

3. Tying wings for Green Drake with large dyed Plymouth Rock hackle

4. *Left to right:* Hardy Fly Hook No. 11. Hardy-Emery Mayfly Hook No. 6. Bartlett B 7362, No. 6. Allcock Salmon Fly Hook 6827, No. 8

CHAPTER VIII

Fly-tying

THE man who said, "Fly-tying cannot be learned from a book" was very nearly right, as it is an art and nothing short of actual practice will bring satisfactory results. It is a progressive art and the flies one ties today will be discarded tomorrow because of the improvement which practice brings. For the beginner the writer would recommend McClelland's book, How to Tie Trout Flies; in it will be found all of the fundamentals for tying both wet- and dry-flies.

The English have always been proficient in the art of fly-tying and have led the way in matters of fly-dressing. The commercial fly-tyers are often limited in their supply of choice materials, which provides about the only excuse that an amateur has for fly-tying. The amateur can afford to be more careful in the selection of furs and feathers, and in case of need raise his own chickens especially for hackles, while the commercial fly-tyer has to take what is available and do the best job possible under the circumstances. In any case, the English know how to tie flies, even if the very best of their flies do not find their way to America.

A small split-wing dry-fly is about the most difficult of all flies to tie properly and from all accounts Mr. C. A. Hassam of the Fly-fishers Club in London was a past master at the art of tying this type of fly. Mr. G. E. M. Skues in his latest book, SIDE LIGHTS, SIDE LINES AND REFLECTIONS, gives an orderly account of Mr. Hassam's method of dressing, and with the reader's indulgence it will be quoted as follows:

1. Fix in vise a small square sneck bend, down-eyed hook, Bartlett B 7362 being the ideal shape, with the eye towards the right and the barb covered by the jaws of the vise.
2. Wax a length of tying silk of the desired color and whip two or three turns on the bare hook in the direction of the tail, leaving only between the first turn and the eye sufficient space to tie down the wings.
3. Tie in by the root, with the tip towards the right, a tiny cock's hackle of good shape and high quality, so that it lies on the far side of the hook with the best side towards you.
4. After two or three turns of the tying silk, break or cut away the root of the hackle.
5. Continue whipping to the tail.
6. Tie in the whisks.
7. Tie in the ribbing, if the fly is to be ribbed.
8. Tie in quill, or floss, if the body is to be so composed; or
9. Spin on dubbing very thinly, if the body is to be dubbed.
10. Wind tying silk to the shoulder.
11. Wind quill or floss (if any) to the shoulder and secure and cut away waste end.
12. Wind on and secure ribbing, if any.

13. Take one turn of the silk in front of the hackle.
14. Prepare two wings, from the best part of one of the best primaries, right and left, of the selected bird (starling, hen black-bird, as the case may be), twitch off from the stalk and match them.
15. Cut away the roots.
16. Push back hackle, so that it lies along the hook with the tip to the left and the best side of the feather facing away from you.
17. Tie on wings with not more than two turns of silk and pass silk over the eye of the hook and under the stump and then under the hook and around behind the wings; attach pliers to silk.
18. Cut away stump of wings.
19. Apply celluloid varnish to the roots.
20. Take point of hackle in pliers and wind in front of the tying silk, held taut, and behind the wings, three turns.
21. Pass silk through the hackle (securing it behind wings) and bring it once over the wing stumps in front.
22. Break or cut away the waste end of the hackle.
23. Finish on head with two turns, whip finish, or two half hitches.
24. Varnish head.
25. Finis.

Mr. Skues mentions the fact that while Hassam always used single wings, he preferred double wings as they seemed to wear better. The writer also prefers double wings.

Many of the American dry-flies are tied with wings of a duck's flank feather, usually mandarin or mallard, and in manipulating a feather of this kind the writer would suggest that a feather with the barbs equally distributed on either side of the center rib be selected and, after stripping away all soft fibres and fluff, the feather be bunched and tied on the hook with the tip pointing towards the right. After the feather is firmly tied into place, the tip should be grasped firmly with the left hand and the feather raised to an erect position, where it should be firmly tied into position by building up the tying silk in front. It is important to set the wings firmly in position, so they will not be forced forward by the hackle which is wound behind them, a common fault. After the feather is firmly set in a vertical position, it should be split into two equal portions and held in that position by figure eight windings of tying silk.

The proper hackle should be selected and stripped of fluff; the length of the barbs of the hackle feather should be about the same length as the wings of the fly.

The shaft or rib of the hackle should then be laid between the wings, with the face or the good side of the hackle down and firmly tied into place; carry silk to tail, tie in whisks, form body, which, incidentally, is often too long—it should not extend back further than a point opposite the barb of the hook; wind hackle and tie off at head with an invisible or whip knot.

Fan-wing flies are sometimes troublesome to tie, but the fault is more often in the selection of the proper wing material than in the actual manipulation. After selecting the two feathers to be used for the fan-wings, and stripping them to the proper size, hold one feather in the left hand, and, after placing it in the position it is to occupy on the hook, tie it into position by winding the tying silk in figure eights in front and behind the shaft of the feather; repeat the operation with the other wing. Then, while the pair of wings is in the proper position, cement them firmly in place by applying lacquer or finger-nail polish; allow lacquer to set before bending up the stubs of the feathers and tying them alongside the shank of the hook. Tie in hackle as above and finish.

Every fly-tyer develops his own methods, and it is not the object of the writer to try to outline any cut and dried method but rather to encourage every one to work out his own system which will, for that individual, produce satisfactory results.

Material Dealers

Probably the most difficult part of fly-tying is the obtaining of suitable materials. This is particularly true of cock's hackles. As far as cock's hackles of a dun color are concerned, the writer has no suggestions to offer, other than to breed them yourself, or to get someone to do it for you; but for the ordinary run of colors and general material, the writer has had very satisfactory results with material obtained from the following concerns:

E. Veniard, 138 Northwood Road, Thornton Heath, Surrey, England, and H. J. Noll, 536 W. Clapier Street, Philadelphia, Pa.

CHAPTER IX

DRAG

THERE are certain trout in every trout-stream that resist the temptations of even the best artificial flies that have yet been devised by the hand of man. These trout are free risers. They will rise and take a natural fly and pay no attention to the artificial floating nearby.

These trout are not especially well educated, although they have undoubtedly had an opportunity of looking over scores or perhaps hundreds of patterns of artificial flies. If a close examination is made of the feeding station where one of these trout is accustomed to lie and have his food delivered by the current of the stream, it will be found, in ninety-nine cases out of one hundred, that this particular spot is well protected by "drag." In other words, this trout had survived, not because of his keen discrimination in detecting the artificial character of the angler's fly, but because the artificial fly did not "behave" like a natural fly.

Trout, when feeding on the surface, are in the majority of cases feeding on the newly-hatched Ephemerida as it is carried along by the current.

The transformation of the Mayfly from the nymphal state to the winged state involves the shedding of the nymphal shuck and a subsequent drying of the freshly emerged fly's wings before actual flight can take place.

These flies have no means of propelling themselves, so they are carried along the current and, of course, their movements on the surface of the water are the result of the action of the current.

Every fly-fisher knows of the multitudinous eddies and whirls which are caused by submerged rocks, and how they affect the course of the natural fly. These well-protected feeding locations of large trout are usually situated near a point where the current sweeps around a large rock. The point of vantage is not immediately behind the rock, which area is so well protected by the rock itself as to become a "dead" spot; but the desirable location where the greatest amount of food passes is the point where the current, which has been deflected by the rock, swings back, behind and below the rock, and meets the current passing on the opposite side of the rock. In cases where the rock is jutting out from the bank, the point of vantage is where the current swings back and then straightens out to continue its flow down-stream.

In order to cast a dry-fly to these spots it is practically always necessary to cast over fast water. This fast current is moving down-stream, while the current or currents behind the rock are often moving across-stream or even in an up-stream direction. When the artificial fly alights on a current moving in one direction and the line and leader on a current traveling in another, it is just a question of seconds before the artificial fly is being pulled or "dragged" by the line and leader. A natural fly acting in this unnatural manner would certainly be viewed with suspicion by any sizable trout. It is said that one small dog can put a mountain lion up a tree, not because the lion is afraid of the dog but because the lion reasons that if such a small and insignificant animal has the temerity to chase him it must be mad, and so the lion climbs the tree to let the mad dog go by.

The trout probably feel the same way about any fly which does not act naturally, and leave it severely alone.

There is a delightful Frenchman by the name of Charley, who, with his bustling little wife, Amelia, runs a small hotel at Analomink, Pa., on the Brodhead. Delightful food, cooked by Charley himself, and comfortable beds make the place a veritable oasis for the fly-fisher visiting that famous trout-stream. In addition, Charley had a free-rising trout in the pool just in front of the hotel.

I had heard a great deal of the beauties of the stream and the week previous to my visit had been shown four Brown Trout of noble proportions which had come from it. I had been assured that there were lots more where they came from, but that they were hard to get. I was not taking my hat off to any fly-fisher, especially as the four fish I had seen had been taken on a fly of my own design, so without ado I set out for Analomink. Charley informed me that I could have my meals whenever I wanted them, and, as there were still a couple of hours of daylight left, I decided to have a try at the fish and eat later.

Charley told me that he thought the fish were feeding,

and it was with some haste that I got into my waders and hurried downstairs. Despite Charley's duties as chef, bartender and host, he seems to have time to show strangers the stream which, in my case, did not take very long as we simply went across the railroad tracks in front of the hotel, where Charley pointed to the stream and said, "That's a good stretch for a dry-fly." Even as he spoke one of the free risers sucked in a natural. That was enough for me. As I scrambled down the hill to the stream I called to Charley to ask how many fish he wanted for breakfast, and he replied that a brace would be ample.

I waded into what I considered to be an ideal position for casting to a good fish that was rising below a rock at the middle of the run, and with the utmost confidence placed a Hendrickson over the fish. The Hendrickson had been selected because the natural fly, *Ephemerella invaria*, was on the water and was being taken by this fish as they floated past the feeding location.

Nothing happened except that Mr. Trout rose again and gulped in a natural within a few inches of my fly. This performance was repeated a number of times before I came to the conclusion that the leader must be too short or too heavy; so I changed to a sixteen foot 3x leader. But this did not induce a rise. Various flies were then tried, March Brown, Fan-wing Royal Coachman, and finally Quill Gordon in small sizes, but none of these flies was any more successful than the Hendrickson which, by all indications, should be the killing fly at this time.

During the time I was changing flies, native fishermen using wet-flies would come by on the way downstream and several of them tried for this fish at my invitation, but "no soap." When it got so dark that I could no longer see my fly on the water I returned to the hotel beaten. Charley was setting up beer for a couple of natives in the bar, when I dragged myself upon a stool to drown my disgust. He, of course, wanted to know how I had made out and it was with some reluctance that I had to admit that I had fished over one fish for two hours and had failed to get it; in fact, had not "put it down."

Charley made some remark of condolence and then turning to his beer patrons remarked that the year previous there had been a fish occupying that same position and that two guests who had been spending a week at his hotel had taken turns fishing for it. Finally, the day before they were to leave, they came into the bar and offered to lay a wager that this fish could not be taken on a fly. Charley said that he slipped on a pair of boots, the stream being then low, took his rod, and, without even removing his white bartender's jacket, waded across the stream to the *far side* and sneaked up under the alders to cast his fly over the "Constant Feeder." He took the fish on the first cast. He had said enough!

The first thing the following morning I, too, waded across the stream. All previous casting to this fish had been from the near side of the stream, and I took this "free riser," this "constant feeder," on my first cast, on a Hendrickson fly, the same fly which had been refused perhaps a hundred times the evening before. But, it was the first time that any fly had been delivered without drag!

Apparently, no one but Charley, who had fished the stream for many years, knew of the almost imperceptible drag which protected this trout's feeding position. However, it was there, and this trout had grown old and fat under its protection. Not a big fish, as Brown Trout go, but an excellent fish for any stream and right in Charley's door yard.

I hope there will be another one there next year, and I hope, also, that Charley will be a little discreet in making suggestions to other guests at his hotel.

AFTERWORD

AFTERWORD

By Eugene V. Connett, 3rd

THERE is little that one can add to a book which covers its subject as thoroughly and soundly as does this one.

One thing I can say: Although never an enthusiast for "exact imitation," I have discovered that such imitation as Mr. Jennings advises is profitable. Throughout the entire season of 1935 I fished with his patterns, tied by himself, and found them practical, taking flies which were pleasant to fish with and which rose fish consistently.

Mr. Jennings' moderation in not introducing a complete new set of artificials to imitate our American naturals, will in itself breed confidence in his knowledge of angling, and his conservative approach to a difficult problem.

It may be worth while to caution the less experienced fly-fisher that no matter how excellent an artificial fly may be, no matter how well it may imitate the natural on the water, skill in presenting it to the fish is still essential. It is just as important to cast so that the leader lies away from the trout, rather than over him; it is just as important that the fly float without the least trace of drag; it is just as important to avoid making the trout nervous or frightened, as when one is using a poorly designed and inappropriate fly.

With the ever-widening distribution of the Brown Trout in American waters, the advisability of catering to his marked preference for fly life, in one form or another, becomes more and more apparent. It is a fact that the Brown Trout is primarily an insect feeder, until he reaches a weight of several pounds, and the angler who is equipped with a practical working knowledge of the insects upon which he feeds, has a marked advantage over his less knowing friend.

That Mr. Jennings' list of artificials will not be added to, and perhaps improved upon, he would be the first to deny. In this book he has shown the way, and has made it possible for others to experiment intelligently. He has not only pointed out the value of first class fly-tying materials, but, in the case of those fortunate enough to have used his flies, he has demonstrated this value in a practical manner.

It is to be hoped that other fly-fishers will undertake to collect naturals in many parts of the country, and that they will follow the practice in collecting, which Mr. Jennings has outlined early in this book. It is possible that we American fly-fishers can prevail upon him to correlate and classify the natural flies on our western streams, if we send him properly preserved specimens with the accompanying emergence dates. Such specimens can be sent him in care of his publishers.

I am sure that I am expressing the views of those who have read this book, when I say that American fly-fishers owe a great debt to the author for having made public the results of his years of work and study, and that we will find an added interest and pleasure in our fishing, armed with the knowledge he has given us.

INDEX

INDEX

INDEX

INDEX

INDEX